LAKEVIEW BRANCH

BM
723
.J8513
1985

Jungk, Peter
    Stephan, 1952–

    Shabbat

R0045825330   8-14-85

DATE		
12.95		

Shabbat

Shabbat

A Rite of Passage
in Jerusalem

Peter Stephan Jungk

Translated by Arthur S. Wensinger
and Richard H. Wood

Times BOOKS

Library of Congress Cataloging in Publication Data

Jungk, Peter Stephan, 1952–
Shabbat : a rite of passage in Jerusalem.

Translation of: Rundgang.
1. Jewish way of life. 2. Spiritual life—Judaism.
3. Jungk, Peter Stephan, 1952–   . I. Title.
BM723.J8513   1985_   296.7'4'0924 [B]   84-40645
ISBN 0-8129-1185-7

Designed by Marjorie Anderson
Manufactured in the United States of America
9 8 7 6 5 4 3 2
First Edition

Preface

I WAS BORN IN CALIFORNIA thirty years ago, the only child of completely assimilated Jewish parents. My mother is from Vienna, my father from Berlin; both of them arrived in America as emigrants. Survivors of the Genocide, they were parentless, had almost no relatives left alive. They married—a new beginning in what they believed would become their new world. I grew up in America, in Britain, France, Germany, Austria. In keeping with the traditions of those around us, we conformed to the Christian holidays. Our maid took me along to Sunday Mass from time to time. I did not know the Jewish Holy Days. My Judaism wasn't exactly kept hidden from me, yet to spare me the horrors of the Holocaust it was given the nimbus of being taboo, a secret which when unveiled would provide no benefit.

Nevertheless, while growing up I asked more and more questions concerning my Judaism. My curiosity was insistent. A Bar Mitzvah was arranged. I learned to read Hebrew (only to forget it a short time later), and I sang the sentences, the paragraphs from the Torah in a Viennese synagogue. Since my birthday is in December, it so happened that the very day after I became a "son" of the Torah we found ourselves celebrating Christmas. I remember our chanting "Silent Night" and "Jingle Bells."

Although my own grandparents had been victims of the Unspeakable, I didn't begin to immerse myself in the literature about the Holocaust until I was twenty-five. By that point in my life I hadn't yet been to Oldnewland; I hadn't yet visited Israel. During my first trip to Jerusalem I spent only a couple of hours in a Torah school; curiosity had led me there. The rabbi at the yeshivah reached out his hand toward me and said, "Promise me you'll come back here; promise me you'll try to find out more about your heritage—here, in this city, at its source. That way you'll make up for everything you haven't known so far." And I did return. A few months later I found myself traveling back, to Jerusalem.

The year that followed has taken shape in this book.

Shabbat

I'm checking them out,
I got it figured out,
There's good points,
And bad points,
Find a city,
Find myself a city to live in.

(TALKING HEADS)

Speak also to the children of Israel
saying: Verily, My Sabbaths shall you keep—
for it is a sign between Me and you
throughout your generations. . . .

(EXODUS, 31:13)

1.

I AM FILLED with restlessness. I go through life with it inside me. Restlessness, my beloved. You are one of my ribs. You are so quiet that I can hear you everywhere. In an average-size room on the sixth floor of an apartment building, suitcases are lying about on the floor, wide open, gaping; next to them, books, papers bundled together, photographs, trousers, shirts, jackets. I share the apartment with Daniel, a tall, powerful young man; we met at a book fair, I was looking for a home, and Daniel said I could move in with him. After I did, we hardly ever spoke; when we did speak, we fought. But Daniel is not the reason I am leaving—I could easily have found another place if I had really wanted to settle down in this city. I want to stay in this city, for the rest of my life. And am not staying! I have been on a journey into the world of anxiety ever since I came from the womb, without an anchor, without a shore; I am the water, I must pitch my tent in the waves.

Daniel's father has come over with his new

*wife Zippora and Zippora's girl friend Judith
and Judith's mother, without letting us know
ahead of time. They have brought along big
jars of gefilte fish and vegetable soup and
boiled chicken; they all want to squeeze into
the tiny kitchen at the same time to warm up
the food; six of us are jammed together there.
"For God's sake!" Judith shouts, because no
one has a match; Daniel has to go over to the
neighbor's, and Judith's mother tells us about
the time when she was little and set fire to a
small hotel on Budapest's St. Margaret's Island, playing with matches. Daniel returns
with an electric lighter; his father thanks him
with a kiss on the mouth, but Daniel bellows,
"Cut that out!" and I run down the stairs to
the ground floor and out into the soft afternoon
air.*

*For the first time, I discover the neigh-
borhood; up to now I have known it only as a
view from the apartment windows. The big
commercial bakery, its height, its breadth, its
black and windowless façade: this is the first
time I have been up close to it. The humming
of the bread-making machinery inside—the
same constant humming is in my ear when I
am sleeping. The factory buildings next door
are silent, nothing stirring there today. At a
dump, I clamber over the skeletons of baby
carriages, remnants of upholstered furniture,
shoe boxes, and cardboard cartons; it is strewn
with white ash, everything quiet, not a breeze.
There is a nickel-plated drawing compass in*

the withered grass—when I was in school I had one almost exactly like it; but I leave them lying there, those memories. A gravel path leads down into a narrow valley, ground bleached almost white, a place for snakes, crusty, the rocks the color of bones. Stone city, surrounded by a hilly landscape of stones. And there flows no river through this city. Little horses are standing motionless under a corrugated-iron roof; no one comes to ride them. I roam among boulders and bushes, above me the dozen high-tension cables of a cross-country power line; I follow the path of the steel towers; the cables crackle gently; even today electric power is being sent out across the country.

Today is the second day of Rosh Hashanah, the renewal of the cosmic cycle, the beginning of the New Year. I have found a walking stick, a weathered, gray fence picket, dry as dust, light as a feather. And all at once, without a transition, it is back again. I had imagined that it was gone, once and for all; but it is back, again circling in my head and in my chest and my stomach: the feeling of being deep inside myself, of having to look out from the inside of myself as through the windows of a building and seeing that I am "I," so precisely shaped and defined. I sit and lie so deep inside me, explore this dead weight of mine as if with insect antennae, touch and sense it a bit more clearly with every step I take. I think: Neon light. It becomes clearer with every step. Tips of my fin-

*gers ice-cold. Neon light is harmful to body
and soul: they will discover that very soon. I
am freezing in the mild light of the sun. Is this
a sign sent to me, telling me not to board that
piece of machinery in two days? The radiant
effect of neon light waves, I am thinking, is just
as unknown as the nature and power of bacilli
used to be, until suddenly they became visible,
magnified a thousand times by the lenses of
optical instruments. Not a cloud in the afternoon sky, the October light dark ocher. . . .*

2.

NEON LIGHT was constantly burning in the
Torah school; on the ground floor and on the
second floor there were no windows, and fresh
air was brought into the little building by ven-
tilators. I wanted to be a student of the Torah,
to cast off my painful not-knowing, to learn to
understand the unknown familiar. I wanted to
make some sense for the crude disorder in my
head, give it a framework. A return to my ori-
gins, to Abraham, Isaac, Jacob; that, I thought,
would be a good way to make embankments for
my shorelessness. Intensification by means of

restraint, for land without shores turns into swampland, I thought, and so I must restrict and focus my strength. I forced myself into "another life." I plotted a revolt against the pleasant ease of my accustomed ways, an overthrow in my own land, a subversion of my habits, a sudden arrest of my tendency to blow with the wind. The day after my arrival—that was twelve months ago now—I entered a Torah school, sharing the dormitory with other young men. Some of them stayed only a few days, some of them had been living and studying here for several years; they wanted to be rabbis.

In the month of Tishri, two weeks after Rosh Hashanah, the Feast of Tabernacles is celebrated, Sukkot, an eight-day commemoration of the wandering in the wilderness, the homeless dwelling in huts whose roofs gave no protection against wind or rain, shelters that had to be torn down each day and built up again the next. They still build them, these palm-thatch booths; the people eat and drink and sleep in them for eight days, turning their backs on home and possessions. During the night following the sixth day, it is the custom to study the Torah until the following dawn. I was sitting next to a stairway railing on the second floor of the *shul* watching my fellow students reading, listening to their loud debates. Returning from the Diaspora, the Galut, they had come together here, searching in the way I was searching; they lived together here and were taken care of, fed, and housed at no cost to themselves.

The reading room was filled with bookshelves and wide tables, the chair backs broken off, rips and holes in the upholstered seats. Many of the books were torn, too, little light-brown threads hanging from their spines. There were also shelves alongside the stairway, running up to the ceiling. On every table, in every corner, were stacks and rows of books. There was an unwritten but strict rule determining the way in which these books were to be arranged: a copy of the Torah could never be placed beneath a copy of the Talmud, the Talmud could never be put underneath a volume on the life of one of the Scribes, and so on. But no matter what, a Bible had to lie on the very top, with the Five Books of Moses at all times above the Books of Kings, or Judges, or Prophets.

Near me there was an argument going on. Without actually understanding what it was about, I nodded in agreement, as if I knew perfectly well what the younger student was trying to explain to the older one. The younger one was called Aron. We had not spoken with one another since my arrival three weeks before; I liked his calm but penetrating eyes, his gently serious manner; I liked his reddish-brown hair, which lay unkempt. Aron's opponent, ten years older and likewise very tall, looked like some minor actor, or a mercenary who had just blown up a bridge; there was something weathered about his appearance. He stood there in front of Aron leaning to one side and sweating, supporting himself on the banister with one hand. He had an artificial leg, which he had called to my attention the first moment we met, but he did not tell me his name; I think none of the others knew what it was, either. I had been avoiding this No-Name. If you told him you were going to the post office, he hobbled along with you; if you took a bus to the outskirts of the city, there he was sitting next to you, wanting to join you on your walk.

". . . because free will is the most precious gift given us," Aron was saying. "But whosoever chooses the good, our sages tell us, chooses life, and whosoever chooses evil, chooses death."

"So then how could you tell me five minutes ago that man can determine nothing by himself?" retorted No-Name. "Didn't you tell me yourself that everything has been preordained, that nothing is in our own hands?"

"Everything is in His hand, everything except our fear of Him. But look," said Aron, "I'm playing rabbi for you and I'm just as confused as you are. Here, look: chapter eight, *passuk* seventeen, what is written there; read it to me."

And No-Name read; I did not want to ask from what book, I did not want to have to show them how little I knew. My grandfather—I never knew him—was a book dealer. His sons, survivors of the Unspeakable, became book dealers, too. I spent a good part of my childhood in their secondhand bookstore in London's Swiss Cottage, thought of the great writers and their works as my confederates; those books are pieces of my own heart. Just to hold a book in my hand, to leaf through it, to feel the leather, the linen, the paper, made me very happy. But as far as I can remember, I hardly ever used to read them. I do not know literature.

No-Name stood propped up and lopsided by the banister and read aloud over the noise: "And the more man tries to seek, the less he finds. And even when the wise man says, 'I know it,' even he cannot find it." He paused a moment to savor what he had read, then spoke. "That's supposed to explain to me the connection between my free will and His control over the world? Well, it certainly does not! He wants us to blind each other's eyes, cut out each other's tongues, before He sends the Messiah to us? He wanted our grandparents to be incinerated?" Aron stared silently at the floor. Was he nodding?

From lack of sleep, I could feel my heart beating in my eardrums. A young boy walked between the reading-room tables, up to a blackboard, took a piece of chalk, drew the symbol for infinity, looked at it, his head tilted to one side. And then erased it. I did not want to feel my heart beating. Did not want to be reminded that the only reason I was alive was that it kept on beating regularly. Yet when I was not aware of it, my heartbeats seemed so natural. As if it had been no more than a piece of fruit, a surgeon once sliced open my stilled heart, sewed up a large hole in it like a rip in a garment, placed the heart back into its rib cage, and since then it goes on beating and beating, at least once every second.

The air in the reading room was musty and damp, like the air in a gym. I was sweating; the others, too. Clothes made of synthetic fibers are like neon lights. We wore white shirts and black trousers and little round caps, *kipahs*, on our heads, all of us dressed just alike. Most of the group had beards (I shaved every day); the signs of solidarity are visible on the outermost layer. I went over to one of the smaller tables where a young rabbi was sitting, a visitor from one of the many other Torah schools. He and the four others with him were our guests for the night. The rabbi, wide awake, rocked the upper part of his body back and forth; after he had read a few sentences aloud, he interrupted himself, then translated the text and discussed it with his four pupils. "You must not trample around in His mysteries," said the young rabbi, and rocked to and fro. "What the Law bids us to do is what we must obey. And whatever is pleasing to Him, will come to pass. . . . Beginning at what hour in the morning are we permitted to pray the Shema Yisrael? Some say when the light is between a pale green and the white-green color of a leek. Others say when you can distinguish between a dog and a wolf, or between a donkey and a mule. And we have united in agreement (may the Everlasting One accept our gratitude) to say the Shema Yisrael when the light is strong enough to recognize an acquaintance at a distance of two paces." I had begun to sway back and forth gently with the others, then got up quickly; the closer I approached the knowledge I sought, the more furiously I resisted slipping into it.

Back to the banister. "Friends! It's four in the morning!" shouted No-Name, so loud that everyone heard him, and he stood there, the same as ever, lopsided and sweating. "One of you produce something to eat, and make it quick!"

"The baker at the New Gate, he stays open all night," someone said, but someone else shouted back from the rear of the hall, deep pockmarks on his face, "Bagels from *him*? Are you crazy?" Why not, I asked quietly, but the fellow with the pockmarks heard me. "How do we know what kind of workers he's got there? Where are they from? His bagels aren't kosher, you know that." "Why not?" I asked again. "The *schmaltz*, you jerk!" he shouted back. "How do you know his helpers don't use schmaltz, huh? Or fat from some kind of animal that's not kosher?" And the others nodded in agreement, repeated the words schmaltz and fat. No-Name said, "It could be, you know, could be they make *treyfene* bagels there. It's possible, we shouldn't risk it." "That—that can't possibly be something in His mind, for God's sake!" I was startled by how loud my own voice was. "Of course it is!" replied No-Name. "No!" I shouted back. "Yes!" he yelled. In anger, I struck the reading table with my fist, and shouted again. The blow and the shout reverberated in me, in the reading room silence. I recalled an imageless dream I had had, very like this moment; sometimes when very tired, one's body recalls things it has dreamed. I had anticipated this moment of outburst in my dream. The silence in the room continued, as if there were such a thing as slow motion even in the absence of images.

After this stretch of time, minutes later it seemed, someone, I knew his name was Mordechai, came up to me, very close. He always carried a machine gun over his shoulder, always. "What is your Hebrew name?" Mordechai asked, and everyone waited intently for me to answer. I said, "I don't know." "What do you mean, you don't know, you have to know it, from the moment of your circumcision. It's something that's told to your parents, what your name is to be in Israel. Right?" I blushed and explained that my circumcision was done automatically, as a matter of course, the day after I was born, and that no rabbis were present. "I'd like to speak to you alone. I'd like to tell you why it is His will that we do not eat *treyf.*" And I knew: Mordechai certainly thought of me as an outsider—no wonder, my light hair, my blue eyes.

No-Name activated a button on the side of his artificial leg so that he could bend it, and sat down next to me on a broken chair. And stared at me. The day before, I had left my Bible lying around in the reading room—was he reminded of that now? A group of students had discovered the book contained not only the Torah but also the so-called New Testament. They promptly decided to burn it, called it the "murderers' book," the name they gave to it because, they said, it had ushered in two millennia of persecution and bloodletting. They had just lighted their little fire in the forecourt when No-Name intervened; he knew, he said, who owned the Bible, and he was going to rescue it from their clutches.

I felt a hand on my shoulder, and looked around; Aron was behind me. "Hey, how would you like to go for a walk with me—right away? We'll take a walk and return?" No-Name was taken aback; even before I could answer, he knew we would not ask him to come along, would leave him there. I got up. At the same instant it occurred to Aron and me that we had to shake hands, and then we were on our way down the stairs, leaving the Torah school without even saying goodbye to No-Name.

The darkness of the night was lighted by rays of cool moonlight; not a star could be seen. We wandered through the Old City streets, down broad steps to the Dung Gate. And farther, outside the Old City walls, below the precinct of the Temple, past tumbled fragments of the City of King David. "My parents, my four brothers and sisters, they're all very strict observers of the Law," Aron began his story. "That's the way I grew up—never knew anything else, never wanted it any other way. To make fire on the Sabbath or turn on a light would have been just as unthinkable as jumping off a skyscraper. Or even to eat anything that wasn't strictly in accordance with the Law, absolutely out of the question. I can understand that business back there a while ago, their outrage, I sure can. If *we* are the ones who were spoken to on Mount Sinai and *we* were chosen to be a Holy People, ah!, a people of priests, and if we have been told what animals we may eat and what ones we may not eat, well, then I can understand how someone who wants to keep the Law, word for word, can get all upset."

Shoulder to shoulder we walked through the half darkness, a little way down into the Valley of Kidron and over to the Garden of Gethsemane. It felt good, physically, to walk along with Aron that way. "Not easy to see why a rabbit, a lobster, oysters, are unclean," he went on in his awkwardly precise, almost fanatical manner, "but that instead we can eat *locusts*! You know, I ran away from the Law, far away, I bummed around in big cities everywhere, those modern Towers of Babel, I lost my form, my shape, my scaffolding. I was no more than a piece of driftwood; then made a lot of money, surrounded by women, all *shikses*, naturally; there wasn't a party anywhere without me. And then, my addiction, my friends died off like flies, ten of them in a single year. And the rec-

ords I produced—they were really big sellers—
got more and more famous. One month ago I
found Susan in a coma, it was an overdose,
rescue, hospital. Then she comes back home,
and . . . in punishment for what she had done,
I . . . yes, well, I just pissed in her face.

"Can't even remember how I made it to the
airport. Sat in the airport bus without even
looking back, at Sodom and Gomorrah, escaped
to the airport to keep from dying. And sitting in
the plane, I knew that it was going to crash. I
thought, if only my parents were dead at least,
if only they had died before me, if only I had
children—essential to make your own death at
least a *bit* less horrifying. . . . I saw it all: how
the plane would bank way over to the left, how
my seat partner, with all her millions of pieces
of luggage spilling out of the overhead compart-
ments, would land on top of me, and except for
a few 'Ohs' and 'Ahs' everything in the plane
would be silent, right up to the crash. And the
farmer, plowing his field down there, he'd
think: first bombs of the new war."

We were climbing up behind the Garden of
Gethsemane to the Mount of Olives, following
a steep, narrow path, high walls on both sides.
Five o'clock in the morning. The air was cool,
smelling of night and dew. "That evening, the
plane landed. It was like being born again, a
celebration: 'I'm alive!' The first week, and the
whole second week, withdrawal, sweat, vomit-
ing. A thousand deaths. And now, a new start.
I'm doing *teshuvah*—you know what that is,

teshuvah? I'm coming back to the Law. And if I take it very seriously, my errors will be forgiven; don't laugh, I'll let repentance really take hold in my heart. I am begging to be taken back into the Law. Ah! It is still rejecting me— yes . . . but I am not giving up, I'll live like a soul, not like a body. I am here to purify my soul, do you understand me? To *purify* it."

We could hear only the sound of our own steps and the slow, rhythmic rasping of the cicadas. I felt secure, protected, walking alongside Aron; how good it is to be together like this, I thought. I wanted to answer Aron, wanted to confide in him. "My parents—I have no brothers or sisters—don't really have a home anywhere," I said, then hesitated. "I grew up in seven different cities. As far back as I can remember, I've been looking for a place where I could live without longing at the same time to be somewhere else, a place that tells me this is home. A city where as soon as I arrive at the station I don't think about leaving on the next train."

"You're just the way I used to be," said Aron. "Never feeling at home anywhere made me yearn for catastrophe. It's because I was full of this feeling of dread—I had run right into the midst of destruction, into the lion's jaws. Like a soul out searching for a body. But this is the city we belong to, our City; it is the body for our souls."

We stopped next to one of the entrances to the big cemetery that covers the eastern slope of the Mount of Olives. I wanted to wander around the gravestones a little. "I'm a Cohen—you don't know what that is, do you, a Cohen?" Aron shouted, half in pride and half in scorn, when he saw what I was about to do. "I am descended from the High Priests, my friend; we Cohens are not permitted to enter a graveyard. I may attend only the burials of my immediate family. I am determined to return to the Law; there is nothing I will not follow now, to the letter. Whoever is a descendant of the High Priests, it is written, shall not make himself unclean by associating with the dead. We'll meet up ahead there," he said, gesturing. "I'll wait for you. Know something? No one is permitted to be cremated—you're buried here without a coffin. Your corpse is just wrapped in a white cloth."

I staggered into the stony sea of grave markers, their white marble glowing dimly in the dark. I couldn't find a pathway; alone in the graveyard, no sense of fear, or of security—I was an empty space, colorless, bereft of thought; no sadness, no joy. Without my realizing it, the light was now between a pale green and the white-green color of a leek. Could I have distinguished a dog from a wolf now, a donkey from a mule? I thought at first I could see a hideous black serpent behind one of the gravestones; saw a poppy standing there and three tall weeds. At this moment between night and day, outside the cemetery walls, was Aron praying the Shema Yisrael? If I could have faith like that, I thought, then I would have a home, and I placed a stone on a grave whose inscription was beyond deciphering. HeSheIt is Creator, Sustainer, Guardian of the Universe? HeSheIt has spoken to us? We saw His words, we heard His images, at the foot of Mount Sinai? HeSheIt never was and never will be, I said to myself then; the weakness of seekers invented Him. I don't need Him, can live well enough without Him. You do not exist, yet I know about You, I heard myself say aloud; I do not know about You, yet You do exist? That was my morning prayer.

At the highest point of the Mount of Olives, we clambered over a wall into the park of a large hotel. The light was pale gray, the voice of a first bird tore through the air, as regular as a heartbeat, sounding like a lament: Zion! Pain! Zion! Pain! The modern white building like some mammoth in the park, a foreign body; in the first light of day, the tennis court, swimming pool, umbrellas, also looked like sleeping creatures. (The hotel had been built eighteen years ago under the former occupation. Those rulers, of a different faith, used some of the gravestones from the cemetery as building material. Yet I could even feel at home in one of the rooms of this tombstone structure; my search for a home even reaches out into hotel lobbies, into hotel rooms.) We stood nestled up against one of the walls of the garden and looked far out over the Desert of Moab, down to the Valley of the Jordan; a chain of mountains formed the limit of the horizon, made a line straight across the land. And over the mountains of sand, narrow strips of cloud, layer upon layer like geological stratification. The light changed from a grayish white to a rosy white; the first stripes of red suffused the lavender clouds, the colors transformed rapidly. The top quarter of the sun's orb seemed to spring from between two cloud layers; from minute to minute form and color changed, the strips of cloud slowly dissolved, and a radiant fan was spread open over the entire view. I heard Aron whispering—was he saying a prayer? A blessing? Akhenaton, I thought, great Pharaoh. You I recognize, you I understand. The fan of light grew narrower, and now its rays shot downward, too. I was bathed in that awareness of being no larger than a grain of sand, but at the same time a particle of the might and grandeur of this sunrise. I was in touch with a fragment of infinity.

"You know those pictures the goyim have hanging in their homes?" Aron asked softly, "the ones where Yoshka is standing in the sky, with rays of light all around him?" It was like a knife in my heart, as if I, through the weird experiences of my childhood, had been a true believer in the God made Flesh. Aron had dared to call my Savior what? Yoshka? You Kahns and Weinbergs, you Levis and Greenbaums, I thought, playing with this idea, you dare to drag my King through your filth, give Him a name as if He were one of you, you God-murderers! I who had grown up with Christmases and rosy glorioles, with crucifixes in cozy corners of the house and along the waysides and in pilgrimage chapels, I was nauseated by this stranger who had been so contemptuous of my shrines.

"*What* did you call Him?" My voice quivered. "You try to mock Him, and then you're surprised that people like you get slaughtered?" But Aron smiled, remained perfectly calm; after a short silence he said, "You want to be absorbed by the nations of the world. You'll take a wife from among them as a mother to your children, and your children will no longer be what your forefathers were—four thousand years, shaken off just like that. You don't really believe that this *meshuggene* rabbi, this Yoshka Pundrak—that's what he's called in the Talmud, I'll show you where it says so if you want to see for yourself—you don't really believe that he is like the Everlasting, equal to the Almighty whose second Commandment to us was, *You shall not make for yourself a graven image or the likeness of anything* . . . anything that is in heaven above or in the earth below or in the water under the earth? Or do you? You really believe that a man, a human being, someone circumcised, with blood and spit and urine and shit in his body . . . that's enough, it disgusts me. It's worshiping false gods to make a graven image, nothing but idolatry, and you've been taken in by such insults to our Immortal God. *You* are His son, *I* am His son, and Yoshka can have been His son for all I care, but no more and no less than I am." I did not know what and

· 21 ·

how to answer him. I felt shame. Were Aron's words beginning to convince me?

The disk of the sun risen completely out of the fragments and slivers of cloud, the regularity of sunrise, sunset, the rotation of the earth on its axis, its orbit around the sun: that morning it all made me aware of my own heartbeat. How could it continue this way for more than a few more days; it would have to exhaust itself soon, wouldn't it, very soon? How automatic, how obvious sunrise seemed to me, as long as I wasn't watching it myself. This eternal rising, day after day. "We have to speak with them, we have to try to build bridges," I said then, cautiously, with a strange, intimidated note in my voice. "They don't really know much about us, nor we about them—yet despite everything, don't we both pray to the same source?"

"Oh, what a noble character you are. But as for loving your neighbor like yourself, Yoshka didn't invent that, you know; he just plucked that one out of the Torah for himself, just like nearly everything else there in that goyishe book they dare to call a New Testament! Just take a look at how he curses the Pharisees, the ones who taught him *everything* he knew, the hypocrite; the scorn he heaps on the greatest rabbis who ever lived on this earth! A false messiah is what he was, a con man. Where is it, that peace he preaches? Where is that love? All I can see are people burned at the stake, crusades, pogroms, murder, slaughter, abomination."

In the hotel park there is a place from which you can see in one direction down into the desert, all the way to Jericho and the Dead Sea, and in the other direction down into the Old City surrounded by its walls. City walls, a girdle of stone, its colors changing according to the time of day, according to the light, from white and beige to ocher and yellow, from brown and gold to a kind of red and gray. We stood there now, Aron and I, the city in dark-yellow sunlight; the guests in the hotel were still asleep, and birds were fluttering around crazily, plunging, racing. When I looked away from the towers, cupolas, hewn rocks, ruins, and looked over again at the unbuilt desert, I thought—for no more than a second—let me out of this present time and into the desert, the woods, out into the plains, away from the cities. Don't look back, don't pause, exodus from culture, save yourself in nature, save yourself from dying when the fire will rain down from the sky.

Descent into the city, mild smells of morning, the warmth of the morning making oaks and cypresses give off their aromas. My feet carried me along automatically, and I felt shrouded in great weariness, as if in a much too heavy piece of clothing. A long distance to cover, blinding daylight. All along the outer side of the Old City wall, past Lions' Gate and Herod's Gate, up the steep Street of the Paratroopers, I hardly glanced to the side. We marched along the entire length of Jaffa Road. In the western part of the city, it was a half-holiday, second to last day of Sukkot; a few shops were open, and from the corner of my eye I saw men with briefcases going off to work and women shopping for food. We crossed a broad boulevard in the direction of the quarter called Kiryat Moshe. I have forgotten the sights, the sounds, the smells we encountered; I remember only that Aron talked about a girl named Lahava who was expecting a visit from him this morning. Aron ordered me not to offer my hand to Lahava or her mother or her grandmother—women were unclean during their periods and you could never know, he explained, whether a woman was having her period. Then we were standing in an apartment, at eight o'clock in the morning, and a few minutes later I was lying on a soft, narrow bed in a darkened room.

I woke up at noon. Aron wanted to go right out to the terrace. The women were cooking; the smell of curry came from the kitchen. I looked into some of the rooms—I look around when I am in other people's places, to see how they live, what kind of furniture they own, what kind of objects they collect. What books, records, pictures. How it smells in the various rooms. On one wall a large poster, black-and-white photomontage: the plateau of Temple Mount, but no remains of the Dome of the Rock or of the al-Aqsa Mosque to be seen—only, high and wide, the Third Temple. And above it the text: "Rejoice and sing, oh Daughter of Zion, for behold, I shall come and dwell in your midst, says the Everlasting." Brown, almost black furniture throughout the apartment, and little elephants carved out of the same wood.

A cube-shaped booth or tabernacle took up half the terrace, its thin walls made of fiberboard, the structure roofed over with great palm fronds and branches, poor protection against wind and rain. In gardens and on balconies and terraces all over the neighborhood were similar huts, all with the same palm-frond roofs. From a briefcase Aron produced four tiny boxes wrapped with black leather laces; he insisted that I put on the phylacteries, the prayer thongs. I said no, thank you, it would make me uncomfortable; I said it seems too weird to me, practically heathen. But Aron insisted: in the Shema Yisrael it is written that the *tefillin* are to be fastened as a sign, upon the hand and between the eyes; that four fragments from the Torah are to be enclosed in the two receptacles, as a reminder of the exodus from Egypt and as an admonition to dedicate your actions and your thoughts to the One Creator, to devote by means of the tefillin your spirit, your heart, your hand to Him alone. I hesitated still; Aron begged me, threatened me, repeated what he had said, a carousel of pleading and refusal, until finally I gave in. "Read to me what is written here," he said, pointing to a page in a prayer book.

"And you shall therefore lay up these words of mine in your heart," I read aloud, on the terrace, next to the booth, in the hot sun, "and you shall bind them as a sign upon your hand, and they shall be as frontlets between your eyes."

"Good. And now copy exactly what you see me do. We'll begin with the thong for the arm and the hand. No, first you have to roll up your shirtsleeve. The four quotations from the Torah are in the leather boxes, the Shema, too—that must lie directly on the muscle of your upper arm. Yes, that's fine, the left arm, so that the box is directly opposite your heart. Please say the blessing after me: *Baruch Ata Adonai, Eloheinu Melech Haolam*, You Who have blessed us with Your Commandments and enjoined us to put on tefillin, yes, and now secure the loop and tie a *shin*, these three strips form a shin, that stands for Shaddai, the Almighty. Now we bind the thong seven times around the arm, down to the hand—right, you're doing it like a pro, definitely not like someone doing it for the first time. So, now the second box goes on your forehead; it must sit directly under your hairline, right between your eyes; it mustn't slip. Ah! You look . . . fantastic, that's the only word for it. Your forefathers are shouting for joy in the afterworld. And now you wrap the end of the arm thong around your middle finger—three times—watch me closely; on the back of your hand you form a *daled*, the second letter of Shaddai. We submit our heart and our mind to Him; we fulfill what is written, that we shall not let our soul and our heart lead us astray. In the old days they wore them all day long, the tefillin. Now let us pray the eighteen benedictions and the Shema. Here, take my prayer book."

And we turned in the direction that our forefathers the world over turned and to where their progeny still turn whenever they pray today: in the direction of the Old City, the Temple Mount, the Wailing Wall. And we began: "Oh, open my lips and let my mouth declare Your praise." I noticed Lahava's neighbors, half hidden behind the door onto their terrace; they had not erected a tabernacle and were studying us as if they were on a trip through time and had just met up with the first dwellers of their homeland. On my brow, a little black receptacle, with four prayers in its four chambers, and black leather thongs twining down to my hand; the hand, too, wrapped as a sign. How peculiar they must look on me, these strange thongs, these boxes. Everything that was "I" was now supposedly bound in unison with the Almighty, and yet I felt HeSheIt to be no more potent, no more impotent, than I did when I was eating, drinking, kissing, when I was sad or jubilant, when I was on a walk or a long journey. No more potent than when I was at rest, no more impotent than in my restlessness. "I do not know about You, yet You do exist?" I whispered.

We sat in the *sukkah* around a little table, and it was hot in there. Carp, sweet-and-sour sauces, vegetables, curried rice, salads, and date cake. Chains made of colored paper and photographs of the Old City taken from the Mount of Olives were pinned to the fiberboard walls. The family had emigrated from Calcutta only a short time before. Aron took a liking to Lahava; I didn't know where or how they got to know each other. "You must not judge a girl by the way she looks," he had told me. "That's nothing more than trying to satisfy your animal instincts when you do that, the beauty of her soul is the only thing that counts, just that; that's what you have to look for. And if her soul does you good, then you'll know: that's the one I'll take as my wife." I saw in my mind's eye the photographers' models, actresses, pop singers that Aron had made love to, had penetrated, and imagined them next to Lahava, who was herself like a plum pudding, a date cake, well fed, dark-skinned, with thick black hair and little scars on her face. Aron gazed at her in that narrow hut, half sad, half proud, as if she were his own daughter.

"Grandmother!" shouted Date Cake. "Come now, we're already sitting at the table!"

"She's all wrapped up in it again," said Lahava's mother, "in my bedroom; she's been praying for hours, ten times a day sometimes, there in that dark room. Mother! Come along now, everything's getting cold!"

Next to me, Yacov, a skinny young man; he was Lahava's brother, on a two-day leave; his uniform smelled of sweat and sand and earth. He hadn't said a word, seemed very tired. "Well then, let's finally hear something from you, and don't make us beg for it, either," his mother ordered, but Yacov ate and remained silent. Sometimes he gave a loud belch; he couldn't help it, and said very quietly, "*Slihah*"—excuse me—and we acted as if we had heard neither the one nor the other.

Sometimes I seem to be able to empathize with the way a stranger must be feeling; I slipped now into Lahava's mind, looked at Aron through her eyes, felt him through her, understood her devotion, felt secure, protected in the glance of his lion's eyes. Aron, you are my home, my reality, I thought; ever since I've known you, you've been a brother's haven for me. By the time we were at dessert, Grandmother came to the table, a little, frail woman. "Tell us something about the Feast of Tabernacles," she asked, turning to Aron. "As a future rabbi, you have to keep in practice with little talks!"

Aron hesitated; it was the first time I had ever seen him timid. "We are not afraid; we are used to living with insecurity," he began, finally, in his strangely precise way. "Through the experience of the tabernacles, we have learned to endure great reversals. The unexpected is our norm, there are no finalities for us, not in this world, except for the One, the One and Only: HaShem. The wellspring of all existence lies on the other side of existence. We are the result of His thought, and therefore we exist. HaShem says to us, 'I love you, I love you truly, behold what I have given you. The only thing I demand from you in return is: fear me just a *little*.' We must thank Him for every breath we draw. HaShem gave us fingernails, gave us skin and hair, our eyeballs, our lungs, everything. He gave us everything. And shouldn't we be prepared to devote every day of our lives to Him? Why do we not pray every day, all of us, glorifying Him and His Torah? Does prayer strike too deep into our pride? Let us live as if we might die tomorrow, as if today were the last day of our lives. How would we conduct our lives then? Fear places me face to face with reality and gives me strength. We should buy our graves when we are thirty-five. Do you understand—a powerful remedy. We have existed without any geographical roots; that is what is so distinctive about us: our restlessness, violent change, always underway. Pulsating, like the light, the light that races back and forth within Him. We have not yet quite arrived in the Promised Land; Messiah has not yet been sent to us; we are still on the way. And our sole anchor? Torah, that is our inner homeland."

Silence pervaded the little hut. HaShem was what the faithful called the Everlasting, "The Name." It is forbidden to utter the True Name; its equivalent, Ad(o)nai, the Lord, may be spoken in prayer but not written out, not even spoken into a recording machine. The paper it was written on, the tape on which it was recorded, could accidentally be lost or destroyed. When Judaism's innermost core, the First Temple, built by King Solomon, was still standing, and then in the Second Temple, reerected after the Jews' Babylonian Exile, the True Name was proclaimed, just one time each year, at Yom Kippur, the Feast of Reconciliation. The High Priest, he alone, cried out the name to the Heavens. One time each year, until 70 A.D., when the Second Temple was destroyed.

"Amen!" whispered Lahava, and Grandmother said softly, "Beautiful, he spoke very beautifully." "*Slihah*," Yacov muttered. And Date Cake told us all about the school she had attended in northern India. She described the view of the Himalayan peaks at night, in wintertime, when it was ice-cold and the air crisp and clear, how the colors of the mountains changed in the light of the moon, how she often spent the night standing at the window and just looking, while the animals in the jungly school grounds screeched and chirped, despite the chill in the air. She said she had felt at home there and often longed to be back.

Suddenly, Lahava's older sister was there in the hut. We hadn't heard her come in, but there she was, standing next to her mother, exhausted and very pregnant. I became embarrassed, as I do every time I meet a woman so obviously with child. As if she had some incurable disease, I looked at her askance, compassionately. She had arrived only after we finished eating. It seemed that the dietary laws were not observed strictly enough in her mother's house—the meat dishes were not kept apart from the dairy products with sufficient care—Rivkah herself would have wanted to make exceptions from time to time. It was her strictly Orthodox husband who had forbidden her from taking her meals at the mother's house. Rabbinical law would have given him the right to divorce her if she had not complied with his wishes. (How was it that Aron could eat here? I asked myself. Was it perhaps that he did not quite observe every last jot of the Law, after all?) Rivkah wanted to sit down. I offered her my chair right away; I didn't want to stay in the hut any longer. "Aron, would you take a picture of him, with his uniform and machine gun?" asked Yacov's mother. Up we got—out of the sukkah that had become a little home for me during those few minutes. Four generations gathered in the hut, I thought: grandmother, mother, daughter, the embryo. On the open half of the terrace Aron took a photo of Yacov, with his peaked cap and the black weapon that hung heavy from his shoulder. Just as the photograph was sliding out of the instant camera, Grandmother walked past us, smiling strangely, like someone fully aware, but with no sense of dread, that her death was near. She disappeared into the darkened bedroom. And color by color, the photograph developed itself in Aron's hand.

Underway, on foot, in the blinding sunlight; pain in the muscles of my legs, my upper arms. I hated to complain about it; I wanted to be strong, resistant; didn't want to feel my heart pounding, but was tired, did feel my heart beating. Aron led me like the Prodigal Son through

Geulah, the section of the city where the strictest of the strict Orthodox live. I didn't want to go to a ritual bathing place, a *mikvah*, with him—it was too much for me, all this in a single day. Aron paid no attention to my complaints. Through the narrow streets of Geulah, past light-colored stone buildings two stories high, scarcely an automobile, children playing tag and hide-and-seek, the boys' braided sidelocks hanging down to their shoulders, the back part of their heads shorn. Their elders wore black trousers, white shirts, black frock coats, and *shtreimel*, the fur-fringed hats worn on high holidays. All the men had full beards and their sidelocks blew in the wind like banners. So many pregnant women in such a small area. And every woman had a cloth over her head or an oversized wig; to wear her hair openly would be an eye-catcher, a temptation. "I'll just wait for you here," I said when we came to a little prayer house. Steps led up to the synagogue room; others led down into darkness. There in the cellar was the mikvah.

"You are coming with me," said Aron.

"I'll stay here."

"You're coming along, now—and high time, too, that you see such a place. You can keep your clothes on, if you really have to, but you've got to see it."

Down we went out of the sunlight. "Very clean here, no question, very clean," Aron whispered. A windowless corridor, lighted by a single naked bulb, and then everything hap-

pened very quickly. We were on floorboard
slats, entered a low room—yellowish tiles
damp with steam, bodies of twenty naked men,
or were there more? I saw sidelocks, beards,
chest hair, pubic hair. Smell of sweat, of feet, in
the hot air. Under the slats, deposits of sand,
grainy bits of dirt. The men looked at each
other's nakedness and then quickly looked
away. Aron took his clothes off instantly. Only
now did I see the pool of water. I had imagined
that a mikvah was a big bathing establishment;
and here, nothing but a square pool, no more
than two meters on a side. Metal steps led
down into the water, into a milky, translucent
liquid, like a mixture of sweat and semen.
Three men were just getting into it; one of
them had large, red spots on his buttocks; all
three descended into the liquid, submerged,
their sidelocks floating horizontally away from
their heads, bobbing next to their foreheads.
They went under time after time, nine times,
twelve times. "You will duck under three
times," said Aron, and I knew then that I would
get undressed; if I didn't he would think I was
uncircumcised, after all—a goy. "The first
time," he said, "think to yourself: I am cleansing my body. The second time: I am cleansing
my soul, and the third time: I do this because it
is pleasing to HaShem."

I stripped and without hesitation lowered
myself into the liquid. At such a time, thought
seems to switch off automatically, or retreats
like a frightened snail into its shell. Hot liquid;

I was standing all by myself in the pool, with the water up to my chin. I saw little hairs floating on its surface, ducked under, thought of the things Aron had told me to say, held my breath three times trapped in this watery torture chamber, climbed out, looked at the nakedness of the other men, quickly looked away, hoped with all my heart that Aron had at least seen the circumcised end of my penis. Used towels lay on the benches, still too wet for drying off. I got dressed and raced out, past bodies with white hair. Standing on the staircase, I realized: it must have been very much like that in those *other* chambers, suddenly to be in a windowless enclosure, no time for reflection, all the others as naked as yourself, everything in a rush at first, no dread—until the door was bolted from the outside.

Back into the sunlight. I, the survivor, the son of two survivors, I am alive—the fact that I am I, Aron is Aron: incomprehensible chains linked together by billions of events. If I should ever produce another life, what a mysterious chain of billions of events will the coming-onto-the-earth of my child be? Where is Aron from? Lahava? No-Name? Every insect, every petal is part of a plan. Each second of each minute is filled with meaning; nothing that has no meaning. And simultaneously, as if it were the very same thought: there is no plan; everything just comes in from outside, pointless events, everything meaningless. In the little synagogue upstairs, the men were gathering, every one of them dressed in black.

Our hair dried slowly. I had taken my cap off after the mikvah and not put it back on again. The sun low on the horizon, we walked in the direction of the Old City. Reddish, rust-brown light by the time we got to the Jaffa Gate and the broad square on its other side; long evening shadows, crowds of people streaming from the gate, others into the Old City; natives, transients, wild bands of youngsters among the nuns and monks; then rabbis, sheikhs, bread sellers, taxi drivers, a family dressed up as clowns; luggage, cameras, crates, fruit stands, orange-juice vendors, croaking voices calling from minarets, from loudspeakers and tape recorders, summons to evening prayer. No-Name's form loomed up from among a group of tourists—he worked as an official tourist guide; he spoke to his audience, with arms gesticulating. He abandoned the group, in the middle of a sentence, when he caught sight of us, limped over to us with long strides. "What luck, what great luck that you're here, oy vavoy! I beg you, wait right here for me—just a few more words about the Citadel, three minutes, yes? Right back; I'm almost finished."

Every time I see a great mob of people, I think that somewhere in this crowd is the one woman with whom I'll want to spend the rest of my life, with whom I'll want to have children. And when I see her, that one woman, I won't speak to her, I'll look into her eyes like an X ray; if she passes by, I'll turn around and stare at her, from her shoulder blades to her heels, and only a bitter sadness will remain. On rare occasions I pursue one of the ones I have chosen a short distance, watching her movements, as if I had been permitted to return from the land of the dead to gaze upon the living but had to remain invisible, couldn't say a word. I see her, she does not see me. But if I had met her today, here between Jaffa Gate and Herod's Citadel, I couldn't possibly have spoken to her—because never in my life did I feel so filthy as I did after that bath in that liquid. I felt as if I weren't clothed in my own skin, as if I'd rented a suit of skin in a shop for bodies, a skin-suit that had been rented out with particular frequency. It scratched me, was too large, too small. I thought, too, that my hair stank, that it clung to my head like wet animal fur. I went up to Aron; his body, his head, had a strong, sour smell, like tablecloths in school dining halls that aren't changed for weeks on end.

"You must help me, my apartment is a catastrophe, we have to put it back in order," No-Name begged us. "I can't go on living that way. We can get it fixed up in no time at all; just the important things, we'll be back in an hour. We can be at the Wailing Wall right after sunset. It's a promise, okay? Good." We made our way through a sea of people which became greater by the minute; the last day of Sukkot would begin at sunset, a holiday, Simhat Torah, a rejoicing in the Law. "Tomorrow the cycle of the week's reading of the Torah will be completed," Aron said above the confusion of voices. "Tomorrow we begin all over again—'In the beginning HaShem created Heaven and Earth.' You must come with me tomorrow evening, and we'll dance with the elders in the street, ah!, wonderful fiddle and clarinet music, I loved it so when I was a child. They take the Torah scrolls out of the synagogues and dance with them; what a day it will be!" No-Name wanted to pick something up at the yeshivah, and so, after thirteen hours, we returned to our starting point. We had come full circle. Aron and I waited outside, looked silently into the reading room bathed in neon light. A poster near the entrance on the ground floor: tanks rolling through a hilly landscape. But these panzers were depicted as phylacteries whose receptacles were the tanks' cabins, whose rolled-up prayer thongs looked like caterpillar treads. "And all the peoples of the earth shall see," it was printed beneath, "that the Name of HaShem rests upon You, and they shall fear You." On the day after I arrived I moved in here, became a pupil, from early in the morning until late in the evening. The yeshivah permitted me to come and go as I chose, and after the first two weeks I took advantage of this freedom, saw Rachel for the first time at a movie house; she was sitting in the row behind me, calm, strong as a magnet. I shouldn't have been in such a hurry to complicate my new life with my old habits. A few days after we first met I moved in with her, began to attend school half-days only, and for a week now had not been a true member of the Torah school community. Aron interrupted my meditations. "You really want to go and help him straighten his place up?"

The route to the Damascus Gate led through covered alleyways; the little shops were already closed, their roller blinds down, and in the air hung a sweet blend of spices, herbs, incense. Bread sellers pushed their green carts past us, donkeys brayed under their burden of gasoline canisters. We walked slowly so that No-Name could keep up with us. "Here, in this notebook of mine, everything is written down, my whole life. My name is Tuvia-Chaim, that means good life. Please, you must read it. I can only tell you that Hannah is the one reason I was born and that she is no longer here, damn it, and I'm the only one to blame. We were driving through the desert—let me drive! let me drive! I kept on insisting—and she gave in, finally; you know what I'm like if I really want something. I fell asleep at the wheel, and when I woke up the car was over on its roof and I was on top of Hannah, not a scratch on me—but she—you understand? The business with my leg, that was long before. . . ."

Tuvia-Chaim stopped walking, and people streamed past us, dark-skinned women selling fowl, the broken wings of the chickens and ducks fluttering insanely, their legs tied together, their heads hanging down. ". . . happened in the Six Day War, I stepped on a land mine, cut off the hunks of skin with my own knife; if I hadn't . . . but what does that matter, compared with Hannah, and I'm to blame, no one else, oy vavoy. I've been saying the Kaddish for her, ever since summer, saying it to this . . . this HaShem who won't even permit me to tear my hair out, or carve a sign into my flesh from my pain. 'Thou shalt not wound thy flesh for the sake of the dead, neither shalt thou shear thyself over thine eyes,' so it is written; I read the passage every day, damn it. I hate Him! I *hate* Him—and the way He plays with us and does everything in His power so that we can't possibly believe in His existence. Read what I have written, please read it, don't let me down. I need you."

"I'm treating you to a taxi ride," Tuvia-Chaim shouted when we got to the other side of the city walls. He was sweating heavily, and we still had twice as far again to go. "Help me get a taxi, quick, or else we'll never get back in time, the sun will be setting any minute." Corner of Paratroopers' Street and the Street of the Prophets, the air smelled like burned rubber. (Were there demonstrations in the Western City again? Were they burning piles of tires in the streets?) Tuvia-Chaim hailed taxis, but none of them stopped; he ran into the middle of the street, waving his arms like a maniac, trying to stop passenger cars, and the more he exhausted himself the harder he tried, his long, lanky shadow breaking over the hoods of the passing cars. As soon as Tuvia-Chaim gets to his apartment he'll take off his prosthesis, I thought to myself; he sometimes did that at the yeshivah and then massaged his naked, red stump. The artificial limb, detached, lying on the floor, with its metal rods and plastic jacket, on its foot a black stocking and a tied black shoe. I did not want to go along with him to his apartment, and, as so often, I concocted a plausible excuse. Next to the curb, Aron had found a woman's gold watch, the name F. Fisch engraved on its back. Why weren't we helping Tuvia-Chaim, why were we standing at the edge of the street doing nothing? A group of people in wheelchairs rolled up to us. The two women with them asked us to help them get the chairs down onto the street and up over the curbstone on the other side. I grabbed the first wheelchair by its front handles, Aron took the rear wheels, but suddenly its occupant grimaced, looked at me crazily, and shouted, "No! No!" I was so startled that I instantly let go of the grips and my whole back froze. Meanwhile Tuvia-Chaim managed to stop a passenger car, and the driver said he would take us a short distance. I told Tuvia-Chaim that he would have to excuse me, I couldn't come with him, Rachel had been waiting for me for an hour, and I finally had to go meet her. When Tuvia-Chaim squeezed himself into the car like a wounded man, Aron bent down to speak to him; he couldn't accompany him either, he said, he was afraid that he would get to the Wailing Wall too late for evening prayers. Tuvia-Chaim was sitting lopsided next to the driver; he slammed the door, rolled down the window, and handed Aron his notebook. He looked at us with a blank expression, but then pursed his lips and waved with a clenched fist, kept on waving as the car made a turn into the Street of the Prophets.

We started walking again, shoulder to shoulder; Aron came with me all the way to my new home near Zion Square. The sun was setting behind the King David Hotel, the mighty structure looming over the cityscape, and then disappeared behind the brick-colored building so quickly and at the same time so slowly, like the minute hand of a clock. As soon as the sun had set, it became instantly cool; fresh October wind blew in our faces. "You'll be coming along in half an hour, won't you?" asked Aron. "You'll bring her along, too? Talk her into it." And I promised him to bring Rachel along with me to the Wailing Wall, though I knew perfectly well that I wouldn't even be coming myself. Where did Aron get his strength from? How could he still keep his eyes open? How I envied him his reserves. I, the child at Aron's side. He, younger than myself by five years, yet my rightful teacher and paragon. It must be his knowing, I thought, that makes him seem so much older. In parting, I wanted to fall upon him, hug him very hard; but since I had promised to meet him again right away, only a quick handshake. I called out an awkward word of thanks before I disappeared into the apartment house.

The stairwell was filled with neon light, even the little elevator was lighted by neon. At least one third of my life has passed—who will be the mother of my children? I thought, as the elevator made its way slowly to the top floor, made its way into my stream of consciousness. I know nothing. I believe nothing. But this past day had made a deep impression on my heart. Then, unexpectedly, this thought: each day, rounded off and complete in itself, is its own being, each day a creation with its own personality. "Each day is a living thing," I whispered; that was my evening prayer.

3.

. . . *IT'S CIRCLING in my head, in my chest, in my belly—the ballast of myself, lodged deep in my center, so clearly measured off and defined on the outside. I sit and lie deep inside myself. And to my surprise, I swing myself up on that very feeling, as onto the back of a beast of burden, and break it, as if it had a thin carapace, like a shellfish. And subdue it. Today I manage that for the first time, thank God. Thank whom? How quickly I speak of Him, without thinking of Him, without being with Him, before I pronounce the word that is supposed to designate HaShem. There, where I grew up, everyone says "Grüss Gott!" when they greet each other. I share the woods, cities, tavern tables, I share the language of the inhabitants of that country and am obliged to forget, forget each day anew, what took place there, forty years ago. I must speak with You in their language, the only one whose subtleties I really know. I beg You, forgive me.*

On this second day of the Feast of the New Year a stony path leads me uphill. In my hand a light walking stick. I reach the edge of a wood; the wonderful, fragrant fir trees were planted no more than thirty years ago, yet they stand firmly rooted in the earth, as if there had always been woods here, in this place, on the barren soil of this land. Next to me, a bush in white blossom, its smell intensely familiar, though I have never smelled it before; it exudes that same feeling of certainty that HaShem was calling for me as when I was standing restlessly beside the gaping suitcases—did You call me? You want to give me a message? HaShem wanted me to hike a short distance out of my neighborhood and make a climb, up one of the hills? Did You call me?

I follow a marked path, the forest floor covered with brown fir needles. A family walks toward me, the three children gathering mush-

rooms. *A tormenting idea: to have to exist at all times for the sake of one's own children— compelled to remain with their mother, so as to be there for one's children. HaShem, I must become a father, like this man? I hear him say the word* leilah; *the night steers a course for the day, I think, it unites; and the day sunders? I am guided by sleep and dream without re- membering their navigation when I am awake? What happened to me before I came into this world? What happens to me when I am asleep? Is that which is written true, that dream is one- sixtieth part prophecy? Is that which is written true, that sleep is one-sixtieth part death? I cling to life, day person that I am. I never want to have to miss anything while on this earth. HaShem lets a stone live longer than a tree, a tree longer than a turtle, a turtle longer than a human. And toy cars made of iron, and this sil- ver ballpoint that I carry around, HeSheIt lets them live longer than the stones. I stop and write in a notebook: "Sleep would not exist if life were followed by nothing. Otherwise we would come into the world and remain awake at all times, until death came. Sleep is prepara- tion." I am forbidden to write today, but go on nevertheless and add: "Because there is a soul in me, I need sleep." Writing is one of the basic activities that are forbidden on a holy day. HaShem will exterminate me from the midst of my people? He will infect me, or someone close to me, with a sickness, because I have written a note for myself today? A girl on a*

*park bench, looking at the view—You want me
to speak to her? You have placed her on my
path? Her name is Leilah? She has lifted her
arm a little and is waving her hand in the air.
"Are you speaking to yourself?" she asks. "I've
been looking at you for a while; you speak to
yourself, don't you?" She looks familiar to me,
and I remember, she works in a supermarket,
helped me recently find radio batteries in the
maze of aisles and shelves. And now she acts
as if we had been destined for each other from
the beginning. "Come over, sit down," she
calls out, and I feel hot in my head and shoulders. I look out toward the desert, over to stony
hills, yellow light on their bald, rounded tops.
The city, high over the surrounding land—it
dominates the Desert of Judea like a mighty
fortress. The girl asks for a light; sorry, I tell
her, don't have a match on me. I stand up close
to her, she smells of light and woods and desert, her black hair is spread out wide. I choose
my words awkwardly, wish her a good New
Year, promise her, too, that I'll come to visit
her at work, and wander off quickly, on a stony
pathway, away from her. Underfoot the fir
needles . . .*

4.

THROUGH STEAM LIKE MORNING FOG I looked
at Rachel, the way she lay there with her eyes
closed; the water burned on our skin, she had
drawn it so hot. I didn't move, inhaled the
clouds of steam; whatever Rachel could stand, I
would have to be able to stand better. I could
feel her legs on the insides of mine, her unknown, familiar body. I wanted to kiss the tips
of her fingers . . . or break the tips of her fingers?
Your beautiful head, your dark eyes, your black
hair—even as a boy it was important to me that
a girl have long, black hair. Your narrow features, your thick lips . . . your ugly face? If my
friends had said about you: air, I would have left
you at once. If they had said: jewel, I would
have clung to you as if to some maternal being.
I have no sister, no brother. When I was a child I
split myself up, into three, five, seven people—
after lunch, instead of taking our nap, we would
sit in the darkened room upstairs and play Par-
cheesi, Happy Families, checkers. It never occurred to me to speak about what I was longing
for, unthinkable to hurt Mother that way. I am

still constantly looking for brothers and sisters, and never find them.

Rachel: I was thinking about you that morning the way I would think about some expensive electric gadget, aggravating myself with my own questions. Had I selected the right brand, the right model? Why this one? Didn't I have a choice among many types and trademarks? A one-year guarantee. With the bigger, cheaper models it could have been three years. The right to return it had lapsed, two-months' trial period over; it was used goods now. Rachel's forehead twitched—she often had that, a little twitch above the bridge of her nose; it helped to stir up my second thoughts. When she slowly opened her eyelids, her calm and candid glance came to me through the fog. Or: were they little eyes, with a dull look in them? I ducked beneath the surface, tasted the scalding heat like a bitter medicine. I got out of the tub. Rachel smiled gently at her victory.

Alone in darkness—it smelled of warmth, every memory of my life stored up in this cave; it contained an omniscience that enshrouded, enveloped me; I could shape nothing, mold nothing. All-knowing but helpless, I lay on a great raft. Rachel pulled up the roller blinds; infinity turned into bedroom, into late morning. A brilliant rectangle of sunlight in the room, half on the floor, half on the bed. Cloudless, light-blue winter sky, in the month of Kislev. Rachel opened a window; the air smelled of hot metal. Our embrace, soft and easy, still warm from the water. I entered you gently in my arousal, incredible, each new time incredible, being able to enter the other person, I deep inside you; I clung to your outer form while parts of me sank deep inside you, we two planets, slipping over into another language, moistening, infusion of weight after weight, neither gently nor harshly. With the ease of slow motion, heavy parts of me streamed forth yet remained intimately connected with me. Is there a way to get closer to HaShem than by becoming such flux and flow? Persistent explorer of your innermost depths, Rachel, I thought: is this why I have come into the world? Microscopically tiny slivers of Eden have been left over for me? But I was not the celebrant, the drowning man I wanted to be; I remained the spectator, a thought was clearly framed: Rachel was replaceable, even interchangeable with the stranger I had gotten to know in a nearby town; no more than a few hours after we had first met, I penetrated her ponderous, scar-covered body. To my horror, that had been no different, Rachel, from today with you. I wished that my first union had been with a person with whom I would then share my life, both of us untouched, a holy deed, and that the two of us had prayed aloud "Shema Yisrael" at our coming together, our flux and flow. Only, no more change and replacement. Alone with this One Woman, to the very end—an end that will come very quickly; life is no longer than a single Uranian year. . . . We lay there; Rachel had spread her hair out. "What are you thinking about?" she asked. "All this time you've been thinking about something, you deep thinker. I can tell that." Rachel's neck near my lips, I liked especially the indentation between her collarbones; I wanted to drink from it. "Enough of this brooding!" she whispered.

The first time I saw them was in an attic, clouds of dust everywhere; they lived in yellow plastic bags, those pictures: all in color, legs spread wide open, firm and flowing, moisture of tongues, ejaculant everywhere. Spent afternoons, nights, with them—how old could I have been? fourteen? sixteen? Couldn't bear going on without them; I went hunting for them in every city, their heads, their tongues; they lived in slick and glossy magazines, and I brought them home for myself. I couldn't distinguish Rachel's face, her lips, from theirs; they stick fast to her; flat centerfolds, once I called for them, I never got rid of them. And they were most successful, they've burned the fibers of my brain, destroyed the path to passion for me. If I should ever be a father, what powers will stand at my side, how can I prevent my son from coming face to face with them, how do I set up impenetrable blockades? I'll have to wage war to stop all contact between him and them. I curse you, barren lovers.

"What *are* you thinking about all this time?" Rachel asked. I looked into the center of her pupils. "Please tell me!"

"Nothing—really, believe me, not a thing."

Stroked her lips and cheeks; then saw myself as a boy in a hotel dining room; there She sat, close by; from the North, her eyes bright, the brilliance of her whole being, I was shaken to the core; through the open windows came the fragrance of an early Italian summer—that was the first time I knew why I had come to this earth. Nothing like that was ever repeated; it took place before my first encounters with those photographs, all in color, before my first sight of those *artistes* of demystification.

Lipstick, hairbrush, slip, perfume, black dress, black silk blouse—Rachel was getting herself ready to go out, just the way my mother did when I didn't want her to go out. "Please, get up, come on, we'll be late, and I really want to go there," she said. "You haven't suddenly decided to observe the Sabbath, have you? Once you start that, it'll get worse step by step, until you're as bad as my uncle. On a trip once, he went to the toilet somewhere; when he locked the door, a light went on automatically—and just so he won't desecrate the Sabbath a second time, what does he do?—he sits there for fourteen hours. Come on, please, get up now!"

All the movie houses were closed this day; public life was at a standstill in the western part of the city. No buses were running; in tall buildings there were elevators that stopped automatically at each floor, so that no one would have to push a button; it was forbidden to complete an electric circuit on this day—that was the same as making a fire, our Sages said, and making fire, according to the Oral Law, was one of the thirty-nine basic activities forbidden on the Sabbath. The Oral Law, they said, was also given to us at Mount Sinai and passed on from father to son for fifty generations, until the Diaspora made it necessary to write down the Mishnah, the Oral Law, the guide by day and by night that explains and expands the six hundred and thirteen commandments of the Torah. This was the mighty flow that carried me along, even after I had half-abandoned the Torah school. I didn't want to go out with Rachel; not on this day. I just lay there on the raft in our room. Three hundred and sixty-five prohibitions in the Torah, corresponding to the number of days in a year, two hundred and forty-eight *mitzvot*, positive commandments, corresponding to the number of bones in the human body—these ground our whole being, on every day of the year, in the laws and duties of Israel. "Please, now, you have to get up finally!" Rachel shouted from the bathroom. We'll have no share in the world to come, Rachel and I, we'll be cut off from our people, I thought. It's either that or bear witness, return to the laws and statutes—*teshuvah*, return. Let us allow repentance to take root in our hearts; let us struggle for the strength to avoid with an earnest will all future errors. And let us then keep watch over ourselves.

The film, a private screening, was shown in the lobby of a new building, which stood next to heaps of rubble and piles of bent metal beams left over from a construction site. The building was finished but not quite ready to move into; we sat on a concrete floor. Patched together with splices, one of the late works of a now deceased director flickered on the back of a prefab wall. I felt a sense of regret and shame at having desecrated this day; thought at the same time, HaShem—if You exist—I cannot believe that You spoke them, those six hundred and thirteen commandments, the way they are written in the Torah, the way they have come down to us in the Mishnah. I thought at the same time: my great wish is to be able to believe, to be able to know that HaShem *did* utter all those words on Mount Sinai. There was a war going on; the two heroes were walking through empty streets; people were asleep in public toilets. As the actors crossed an empty park wet with rain and saw in the distance a mountain peak on fire, I was there in the park myself. On a sidewalk, half in sun, half in shadow, I patrolled the borderline with the actors. Then it was evening, the light milky. After the film was over I sat there motionless, everyone quiet all around, as at the end of a service. Someone who knew Rachel bent awkwardly down to her and said softly, "Words are bullets."

Light-yellow stone buildings, metal roofs, a park, tombstones—still enveloped by the film, I carried it out with me into the painful brilliance of the sun. Rachel (not replaceable, a heroine) and I walked ahead in silence. A white blossom on the sidewalk, two yellow beetles next to it, palm trees in the gentle breeze, two nuns, eyes downcast; heavily armed soldiers ran past us; excavation for a new building, deep as an abyss. All simultaneous, all one. A woman with short hair came up to me, asked me to lend her my ballpoint, as if she knew for certain that on this day, when writing is forbidden, I would have one with me. On every television antenna within eyesight perched little black birds, not a space between them, every inch of every antenna occupied by their throngs; the multiarmed crosses struck into the sky like magic signs.

All by ourselves in the streets, shops closed, a great cloister nearby; we aimed for it. From a side street the clamor of a burglar alarm; no one came to turn it off. The totality of the scene broke down into little separate images—an intimate feeling for something unknown. Everything familiar was transformed into things seen for the first time: the buildings, their individual floors, windows, roofs, chimneys, all as if unknown.

"We rule the world for six days," I said abruptly, "and on the seventh, our minds are supposed to be engraved with the thought that it is not we but the Everlasting who is the Creator and Ruler. We are supposed to give the world back to him, so to speak; we've only been borrowing it. At least one day a week, all interaction with nature is to be interrupted; we are not to act out any thought with regard to any object. Time is switched off. It is written that on the Sabbath we receive a second soul; but we don't feel it, naturally, because we're listening to the radio or carrying money around with us like any other day; or we absolutely have to go see a movie and make ourselves breakfast like any other day. . . ."

"It sounds like something fresh off the printed page, the way you're talking. It sounds so quoted—like something not really in your heart . . . but I'm beginning to know you: when you're with strictly Orthodox people—listen to yourself sometime—you're the one without any faith. And when you're with the unbelievers, you're suddenly playing the rigid believer. It only takes a little while and you shift over to a different way of looking at things; you're a slow-footed chameleon—one day this person is right, the next day someone else is your model, as long as he has charisma, a 'personality.' Just put a little faith sometime in what you are yourself: your own center is not going to come to you from somewhere outside. If you stay the way you are now, there'll never be any mystery about you. You're like an actor. I never know, *do* you have the strength or not? When we meet each other in the grave one day you'll still be wringing your hands and wailing, 'What's going to become of me?'"

I wanted to blot out the fact that Rachel's words were hurting me and I searched my mind for memories, for associations, but she had already started up again. "Aron is your model right now; he keeps the Sabbath holy and so you want to keep it holy, too. Not because you believe, but because Aron follows the letter of the law. You're in awe of him. Pretty soon you'll be telling me the world was created in seven days, six thousand years ago. When I say to my uncle, 'You, Yehetzkel, people were on this earth a million years ago, in the course of evolution,' then he looks at me with such incredible sadness in his eyes that I begin to talk about something else right away, about the library, my work there . . . but in his case that's all *genuine*, not so half-and-half as with you. Not long ago I said, 'You, Yehetzkel, do you know there are wonderful cave paintings, at least thirty thousand years old for sure?' 'For sure?' he said. 'What's that, for sure? You were sitting there maybe while they were making the pretty paintings?' . . . Sticking to the law! That's just fear of freedom. He doesn't exist, that Everlasting of yours, and I don't need him, either. I live very well without him. If he had been around, our grandparents would still be alive; *they* stuck to the law, a lot of good it did them, a people of priests, a light to the nations, *his* people! It's remarkable how much he had our welfare at heart."

We crossed over into another country, late in the afternoon; the border between the Western and the Eastern City was an invisible transition, no no-man's-land between them. Shops all open, lively noises at a bus terminal, tape recorders playing flute music, children in school uniforms running from candy stands to fruit shops, from coffeehouses to bookstores. Men and women in long embroidered robes, black and white, red-and-white *kaffiyeh* shawls, or white muslin veils wound around their heads. In Salah-ed-Din Street it smelled of spices and gasoline, fresh flatbread, cut flowers, and neglected public toilets. In displays along the main street, strings of little colored electric bulbs flashed over wooden mangers and cows and sheep. Piles of Korans bound in red plastic. The distance from Rachel's house to the "other city" could be traversed in ten minutes, yet in the years she had lived here Rachel had very seldom crossed the invisible border. "It's like an airtight curtain hanging in space, like a powerful electrical field," she said. "Where the real border used to run before, when I first got here, high, ugly walls . . . that's not there now, but I can still feel it. Do you know that film where the guests at an evening party are locked together for days in a big room, and they can't even get from the one half of it to the other, even though there is no visible barrier at all to hold them back? All of us go into the Old City without even thinking about it; but we really almost never go into the Eastern Sector." A young tourist who was buying corn on the cob in a little shop was following with his eyes every movement Rachel made. I wanted to take hold of her, wanted to show that I was escorting her as my property, my showpiece. And in reality her guided missiles were still deep in my body—words are bullets. She wouldn't let me put my arm around her. I recognized her supremacy and had no counterweapon. I thought: a relationship is a profession; we are two halves of a city, separated by nothing but an invisible curtain, yet it is made of stone.

Through Herod's Gate into the Old City. We drank strong coffee, watched children burning bundles of paper under a dark archway. In Hebrew, Rachel asked a man selling camel-leather bags where she could buy good fresh meat; he didn't answer, kept on reading his book without looking up. When I asked the same question in another language he immediately left his stand unattended, accompanied us through narrow streets like stairways, through the dusty light that stays the same all day long in the covered *souks*. Past leather tanneries, tea, tobacco; all pedestrian lanes, no automobiles in the Old City. He took us to his friend, the butcher Ahmad. In his white-tiled shop great hunks of skinned animals hung from metal hooks; on a wooden table sheeps' heads, neck arteries, mucous glands, windpipes, shining eyes, sharp-pointed maws, everything without fur and without skin, flies everywhere. We bought some lamb, carved right from the carcass. A ram's testicles dangled from the tatters of its former body. A few steps away, the Church of the Holy Sepulcher—we approached the coarse gray building in silence, holding our meat and corn in a paper sack. We made a pathway through countless bodies, a throng of people without fame, without excellence; there cannot have been very much more in their lives than their pilgrimage here.

In the Church of Churches, in coolness and darkness—how Aron would curse me if he knew where I was now. Even at the height of the summer heat, our forefathers would avoid the very shadow of a church. Their children spat upon crucifixes, in the fields, out in the countryside; the elders stamped on the ground whenever their way led them past a cross. And we two, their descendants, here we were in this lofty space at the season of Advent. Priests were rubbing silver objects on a stone tablet; after the Deposition from the Cross the Circumcised One is said to have been embalmed here; women in black knelt before it, wiping the marble with handkerchiefs, flower petals, plastic crosses, kissing the stone. Did these supplicants know that this red tablet had been set in place here in the year 1810 after his birth? Not far from an old weeping woman a group of tourists was gathering; they had red-and-blue hats with signs on them saying "Hello!" I told Rachel that I was proud and happy not to know where Moshe Rabeinu lies buried; no one has discovered *his* grave so far, no one will ever perform idolatry there, or erect some building for the purpose of idolizing a human being.

Vaulted cellar, first floor, second floor, attic chapels—six different congregations shared this gloomy labyrinth; the Church of the Sepulcher is the size of a small city. Rachel was very quiet, asked no questions, reserved any opinion she may have formed. Candles, floral decorations, icons, statuettes, resplendence of silver, bronze, gold, platinum. Crosses scratched into the massive walls by the Crusaders. I was unable to get that one sentence out of my mind: You shall make no graven image, nor the likeness of any thing. You shall not worship them; you shall not bow down before them. Diversions, interruptions—they destroy the Direct Path to HaShem; simplification, mitigation, debasement of the Eternal Work. For a prophet was so insolent as to speak in His Name things that HeSheIt had not commanded him to. Past a richly decorated chamber—there, they say, was the rock-hewn tomb; the strangers stood waiting in a long line, faces flickered in the light of candles. It seemed to me that Rachel hesitated even to look at the burial place. Was she afraid to enter this strange room of worship? "No, I don't want to." She actually pulled me away. "Not in there, absolutely not." I had to laugh. The refuser was refusing to enter the tomb of "Yoshka Pundrak"? Refused to count herself among the idolaters? She looked at me, sad, embarrassed. From the background the voices of a choir, resonant bells, organ music, the sounds of all the congregations at once. A woman was following along after a priest who was swinging censers. A bearded man sat next to an icon: "Many people on their journey here; a sickness, a cancer, those travelers, they are destroying the earth."

Twilight was rapidly descending over the

city; taste of oil, wax, incense in my mouth. Rachel was looking in the narrow alleys for fresh thyme, bought two bunches of the herb from an old man. His black, wrinkled hands had a second skin over their skin; it looked like a very thin glove. "Now you'll start laughing at me again," said Rachel, softly. "If we—I'm amazed I want to—but if we go straight ahead, down there—that's the way to the Wailing Wall. Don't look so astonished. I'm serious. What do you think my friends would say to that? None of them ever goes there." My only concern was that I didn't want to appear at the Western Wall with the things we had bought; desecraters of the Holy Day—buying food on a Sabbath, when even carrying something is forbidden. I looked like some goy just passing through, with a package of meat in my hand, forbidden meat at that, not even kosher. We took the packages to the man selling the leather bags; he was reading in the Koran, didn't even look up, just nodded, fine, fine.

High wall made of light-colored blocks of stone, broad band, the most significant symbol of the inextinguishable existence of the People of Israel. Above it, however, on the open space of the former Temple precinct, on the Hill of Moriah, for thirteen centuries: the Dome of the Rock and the al-Aqsa Mosque; this wall of hewn rock the last remnant of the Second Temple. Soldiers on guard, strict security; we slowly crossed the broad square toward this tangible nucleus of Israel. I had to part from Rachel. At the entrance to the men's side, a custodian handed me a black cardboard cap. I arrived at the stone, my loftiest place on earth, saw tufts of grass growing from the crevices; little pieces of paper were sticking out from between the stones, prayers of supplication and thanks. I touched the dryness, the porosity of the hewn rock, I kissed the stone (idolatry?). My addiction to belong has led me here, it is fixed incessantly in my mind: I cannot think of nor pursue anything else.

A high metal fence separated the two sections. I climbed onto a wooden bench; Rachel was standing there among the praying women, without moving, arms tightly folded. Girls were reading their prayer books, gently swaying, many of them touching the stone as they read or placing their foreheads against it as if it were a living thing, its own genus and species. "Rachel!" a girl with curly, light-blond hair suddenly called out; she had been standing beside her. "Edla?" cried Rachel, and they hugged each other. Edla pressed her prayer book to Rachel's body—and then came a cascade of words. What torment, not to understand all the languages of the earth! Language of Man, most noble concept of history, great uniform force, shattered into a thousand fragments at Babel. If a workman fell while the Tower was building, his loss was not lamented, but if a single tile fell and smashed, the workers sat on the ground and wept. HaShem, You who demolished simple Babel, You do not come down today when

Babel holds sway thousandfold? If You existed You would not let this earth keep standing. Or are You waiting? Will You let all who ever lived be gathered together on the earth before You descend once again? The Great War was the final warning to us to turn back? And we did not turn back. You are waiting.

I left the metal partition, moved past the faithful all dressed in black; they were reciting the prayer spoken when the Sabbath ends. *"Ma'ariv,"* a rabbi called out to me, evening prayer; but I didn't stop. The great wall of ashlar—visible edifice of thought—the people along it praying as if glued to the very stone. I pictured to myself a union of the wall and the bodies of the supplicants; together they were transformed into a single being. And the bodies of those not close up to the wall—that evening they seemed to me like some sort of construction scaffolding or vehicles, like sanctified forms of locomotion in which their souls resided. That swaying motion as they prayed, did it enhance the power of prayer? Did it multiply their concentration? I was filled with envy at the praying of these men, at their ability to feel so deeply. They are not believers, they are *knowers*, they *know* that HaShem spoke to Moshe Rabeinu in the Desert of Sinai. Something good and obscure, good and ponderous, good and discordant emanated from them. Are they the elect, are we chosen to announce to the world: verily we say to you, behold, and you shall know, Messiah has not yet come! Is such a cry my mission, too?

A cavelike hall of stone, at a side angle to the Western Wall, damp and cold, illuminated by weak lightbulbs; only the men may enter. *"Ma'ariv!"*—these knowers (paratroopers and members of the tank corps among them) gathered around their rabbis; boys were playing tag among the tables and piles of books; an old man was telling a group the story of the Prophet Ezekiel as if he had been there himself. I wanted to pray, didn't know how to give thanks for being here on earth, thanks for eyesight, hearing, smell, touch. I felt ashamed praying aloud. I didn't pray, stayed at my own ground level, without the strength to reach a higher plane. "Oh, how good that you're here," someone called out in a deep voice. Tuvia-Chaim was standing next to me, the good soul, sweating and lopsided, "I must say Kaddish, for Hannah—I'm so happy you're here, we'll join those over there when they're finished—they're still busy separating Holy Day from the rest of the week—then I'll go through my prayer; damn it, I never even said Kaddish for my own father, but for Hannah? For Hannah—how many months now? For six months. Pay attention, the passage is coming up right away; look out now. So good that you're here, forgive me, I have to hold on to you, your shoulder; what a torture this life is." Tuvia-Chaim said the Kaddish, the prayer for the dead. But he didn't know it by heart, even though he had to say it three times each day. Why didn't he use a prayer book, couldn't he read the print? I supported him, felt his body trembling. Those with the Knowledge turned around and looked at him, called out parts of the prayer for him, which he then repeated haltingly. Fighting back sobs, he imitated the words, the intonation, making mistakes constantly. Why were there no tears in his eyes? I observed myself observing Tuvia-Chaim, calmly, cold as metal, made mental notes for myself on the way he was breathing, moving, without an iota of commiseration. I the magnanimous commandant of the camp, he, a prisoner with a tattooed number on his forearm, approaching me. I exhibited my sympathetic side, was the heartless helper, and Tuvia-Chaim was thanking me for being here. I propped him up, stroked his shoulder, his back, his arms, held his hands. I the bastard—false, homeless bastard.

The Wall, now bathed in artificial light; Tuvia-Chaim at my side. He wanted to come with me, wherever it was I had to go. On the great square, I was looking for Rachel, wanted to get rid of Tuvia-Chaim, just get rid of him. " . . . so woeful and sweet, don't you think?" I heard a woman say. And her companion, "Feelings are so much stronger than any control one has over them. . . . " A soldier, "But Rabbi, where do you know me from?" and the rabbi answered, "We met at the foot of Mount Sinai, on the day the Torah was handed to us." And a girl with her arm in a sling, "It was awful, just awful, imagine such a *dumpy* life-style." And someone wanting to take down a telephone number, but the other person said, "First, *Hamavdil*—repeat it after me, 'Praise be unto you, Everlasting, King of the World, Who distinguishes the holy from the profane." Thus did they part the Sabbath from the rest of the week. "Really, wherever you go I'll go, too," Tuvia-Chaim whispered, and I kept looking for Rachel, finally found her, with Edla, at a water fountain. "Imagine, meeting Edla, I've told you about her, haven't I?" said Rachel, keyed up as if she had had several cups of coffee. "She's getting married today, now, in two hours she's getting married. It's very unusual, Edla says, right after the Sabbath with no time to really get ready for it, but it's got to be today, because her parents-in-law suddenly have to go on a trip, first thing tomorrow."

Tuvia-Chaim, as if he had been yanked up out of the ground, roots all tattered—I should have been holding him up; he was searching for something to say; we stood there without a word, looked at him: do we hate our neighbor as we hate ourselves? How hard it is, love of neighbor. Not until this moment did my utter lack of feeling for Tuvia-Chaim turn to sorrow and wound me. This would have been the time to stroke him, console him, but now I was incapable of anything. My squandering of fake, half-hearted feelings was taking its revenge now. Tuvia-Chaim, forgive me, I beg you, forgive me, you twisted piece of wreckage; you wanted to stay with me this evening, and I wanted to get rid of you as quickly as possible. He was shocked when he saw that I hadn't come here alone, and when he heard the words "getting married today," the dead woman arose in him. Tuvia-Chaim wept; this time I did see his tears; they filled his eyes, ran down his face, into his sparse beard. Me? I can't cry, was even unable to cry at the funeral of my best friend. I tried very hard to exhibit my tears to his family, but couldn't—from pride at still being alive while he was dead? Is there always a bit of *schadenfreude*, of malicious pleasure, in me when I witness the pain of others' suffering? At the movies I cry on the slightest pretext, floating on tears through the story on the silver screen.

The four of us, speechless. I stared at a big sign in three languages that forbade anyone from going up onto the Mount of the former Temple. Since we do not know any longer exactly where the Holy of Holies was located, the faithful do not enter the precinct where the Dome of the Rock and al-Aqsa Mosque now stand. I looked at the pistol that Tuvia-Chaim, tourist guide, always carried on his belt. We didn't move until Rachel, gently but firmly, began to talk to him and touched his powerful body, while Edla carefully avoided coming into contact with any part of him. Mordechai, fervent student of the Torah, whom I had first met that night when Aron and I became friends, Mordechai was patrolling some distance away, rifle over his shoulder. "Don't forget," he called to me, "we have a date," and then we waved at one another as we had done ever since that first encounter. There are some people I'm fated to meet, an affinity, beyond any categorizing, which puts us into invisible nets—determined from the very beginning of things. The knots of my net have always been there, all I have to do is discover exactly where they are; all they have to do is get into my hands. In the life to come, this meeting each other will go on; the cautious but joyous, the guarded but excited feeling of being together with friends in this life is a presentiment of the happiness of reunion after this world, the anticipation of a future sublime meeting.

Edla hurried away, her mother, her sister, aunts, cousins, girl friends were waiting for her. Tuvia-Chaim staggered back to the Western Wall; I watched him go until he disappeared among those still gathered there. As if Rachel were the only person I had in the world, I embraced her body in the white darkness, pressed her to myself. She hugged me hard, her two hands tight against my back; good that she was there. You daughter of the Everlasting, is it on your account that I came into this world? You interchangeable Everywoman, you have fallen to my lot, I to yours. Will we stay together, all our lives? If you should fall to Aron's lot, and I to Edla's, would that make a difference? Is it all the same who the one you embrace, the one with whom you are entwined, is? As we were leaving the great square and slowly ascending in the direction of Mount Zion, Rachel said: "Edla used to be just the way I was, even more, the real unbeliever in our class; she even tried to wean me away from my half-hearted faith in those days. That's wild; little Edla, the last one you'd ever expect . . . that's really weird to me. . . ."

A narrow street alongside Dung Gate, steep climb; with every step we took, the view of the illuminated Old City widened out in the center of the Temple Mount the golden gleam of the Dome of the Rock. Lights went on in the villages to the south, glimmered like stars fallen to earth; scratchy wailing of the muezzins' singsong from loudspeakers in the minarets, shattering the fragile evening stillness. Far in the west there was still a dark-blue strip of daylight. Then two yellow lights in the sky, over the Mount of Olives, high above the desert. They were stock-still, motionless. Some kind of toys? Airplanes? Flares for military exercises, shedding light from the sky on a theoretical nighttime battlefield? As she did every day about this time, Rachel took a strip of cellophane-wrapped green capsules from one of her pockets, swallowed a pill with the saliva she had accumulated in her mouth. Even though the last thing I wanted was to have a child with Rachel, it was on this evening that I first grasped something that had been only a vague feeling up to then. In the light of those yellow flying objects, I knew this pill bore a heavy burden of guilt; it cut the fragile fibers, tore the mesh of genuine sensation as vehemently, in its way, as those idols in the slick and glossy magazines had. I said nothing of what I was thinking.

Angular juxtaposition of dark buildings: King David lies buried here, according to the legend. The Diaspora Yeshivah on Mount Zion was set up next to his tomb, overshadowed by the nave of an enormous church that made the darkness darker still. Edla was to be married this evening to a fellow from this yeshivah. He had been studying here for five years, planned on becoming a rabbi. Relatives, friends, acquaintances on both sides had assembled here in great number, were strolling aimlessly through the night, past gardens and on through dark passageways, carrying candles. Women and girls were standing together, or ambling in groups through the darkness; boys and men, too. Rachel had wandered away somewhere. I didn't look for her but hastened off with other young men nowhere in particular. A high-pitched voice kept crying, "Oy, oy, oy, oy!" With three others whom I couldn't recognize, I searched for the source of this bloodcurdling sound. We got closer to it— in a low-vaulted room (the skin on my temples froze) candles were flickering in niches. Stone tablets, countless stone tablets, let into the walls, every tablet with the name of an eradicated community, a demolished village or town. The cry stopped. *One could see through a peephole in the door that the ones standing closest to the injection slot instantly fell to the floor dead. One can say that approximately a third died at once. The others began to stagger, scream, and struggle for air. The screams, however, soon changed to death rattles, and in a few minutes all lay dead. After twenty minutes at the most no one moved. . . . They covered the entire floor, most of them squatting on their haunches and clinging to one another.* Next to the stone tablets, in a glass vitrine: a shirt made of Torah-scroll parchment, and a little decorated drum stretched with the skin from a forehead. "My God, my God, why did You forsake them? My grandparents cried, but help was far. You did not answer."

Outside again. Full moon. A high convent tower. A rock-and-roll band was playing off in the distance, stopped, began again. Two figures under an olive tree. I heard men's voices, approached them. "Never knew it until yesterday. Do you know that Rashi commentary on why Havah was created from Adam Rishon's rib? No? Because they first came to earth as *one*, grown together like Siamese twins." "No! Fantastic!" the other interrupted. ". . . and so if it is written: This at last is bone of my bones, flesh of my flesh; she shall be called Woman because she was taken out of Man—that means that HaShem separated this fused, hermaphroditic creature at the midsection and made two different creatures from it." "No! Fantastic!" the other repeated. They got up; I followed them, soon saw them surrounded by

· 71 ·

twenty, thirty men; they placed a white shawl around the first of the two who had been speaking; the cloth shone in the moonlight. The men sang in chorus, *"Bo-i Kala! Bo-i Kala!* Welcome, Bride! *Bo-i Kala!"* We progressed through labyrinthine buildings; someone put a kipah on my head; we got to a brightly lighted square in front of a small synagogue. Under olive trees and pines, girls and women stood together, awaiting the bridegroom, who then arrived, half pushed, half carried. Rachel was among the older women, an empty wineglass in her hand. I wanted to speak to her, touch her; at the same time wanted to forget her, lose her; she did not look at me; I wanted her to see me, simultaneously was happy to be invisible. I, the butterfly, swept through the real world; yet real butterflies go through their caterpillar and pupal stages—before their new life they have at least been anchored somewhere. But me? From one kind of fluttering to another, shoreless, anchorless; from being like a butterfly to being like a leaf in the wind, and back to being a butterfly. The men sang *"Bo-i Kala!"* swayed back and forth, arm in arm, like moving water, a wave of men facing a wave of women, two armies before a battle in the desert. In the midst of the women's wave was Edla, little Edla, in a white gown, a veil covering her face.

Near the balustrade of this elevated square, the *hupah* was being put up, a baldachin made of silk, carried on four poles, a portable heaven beneath heaven's vault. The wave of men accompanied the groom, reading aloud, praying, reassuring him, among them the rabbi, a young man with a red beard, chanting in a deep voice. The wave of young women was now leading Edla to the hupah; for seven days she hadn't been allowed to see her betrothed. Three women stayed with her under the baldachin, walking seven times in a circle around the groom and holding tall candles, while the rabbi intoned his rhythmic chant. A melody, strange and familiar as a dreamsong. As the ceremony ran its prescribed course, I tried to move up closer, wanted to stand right next to the bridal couple. Saw the shining beauty of the man, and the pale minuteness of Edla, her soul the bridegroom's core: it was that untouched core he desired to wed. Yishai, lucky man, you're ahead of your time; there will be a return to your example, your model. Your purity must be reinstated, resurrected. "Among the peoples of ancient times"—the rabbi chose his words with hesitancy, set them like little stones in a mosaic—"the wife was treated as the property of her husband. Husbands were the slaveholders of their wives. But the Almighty—praised be His Name—put an end to this situation. HaShem invested matrimony with holiness. He created the wife as a helpmate, as a coequal companion. He did not create her in order to satisfy the husband's desire. He must dampen his appetite at particular phases in the life of his wife. It is not he who rules over their life together, but the Almighty—praised be His

Name—who gave us the Torah. It is He who prescribes and determines how man and wife lead their life, the one with the other." During the rabbi's sermon I managed to get to the balustrade, realized only now that this square was directly above the memorial site where I had been standing a short time before. Beneath the full-moon sky filled with stars, above the cellar of ashes, I married. We shall have children one day, we children of the survivors. What we call chance is really the language of HaShem. The rabbi was saying, "Since the earliest days of our history the woman has been chosen to climb to the highest step. Let her be judge, let her be prophet. Did not the Almighty crown Miriam, sister of Moshe Rabeinu, as a prophetess? Have not women been permitted to ascend the throne of our Kingdom? Is it not written that in the Age of the Messiah it will be the ideas of woman that will rule the world? Are not women—we ask each day anew—are they not nearer to HaShem than we men?"

The rabbi's speech ended in a barrage of flash-bulbs. The waves of the men and women were suddenly mingled; the groom's mother gave instructions for a small movie camera to start shooting; Yishai placed a gold ring on the ring finger of Edla's right hand, then crushed a wineglass underfoot, a sign of mourning over the destruction of the Temple. As Yishai put his signature at the bottom of a parchment document, the young men sang and danced around in wide circles. Red wine was drunk beneath the hupah. I saw no kiss exchanged between bride and groom. Now the dancers raised Yishai to their shoulders, encircled and cheered him; they sang the same refrain in English over and over, "We want Messiah now. We want Messiah now. We want Messiah now. We don't want to wait"—the same stanza over and over. *"Mazal tov!"* everyone shouted. *"Mazal tov!"* Between shouts I heard someone say, "The suffering of the soul cures the heart." And a voice farther away, "The husband fires off the ideas and the wife lets them grow and mature," and another voice, "You mustn't harm your neighbor even when you know you're absolutely in the right." The bridal couple withdrew for a few minutes. This brief moment alone together is the real marriage bond. " . . . we don't want to wait," a few voices were still singing. I heard, ". . . the hymen . . . well, how should I put it? Well, basically the man fulfills the creation of the woman, when the hymen is . . . " I saw Aron not far away, ran over to him, threw myself at him, like a child, I embraced him impetuously, so happy to see that he was here, too. Yishai, the groom, it seemed, was Aron's distant relative. Rachel suddenly stood there between us. "That's her?" Aron asked. I nodded self-consciously. "And you get along together well, the two of you?" he asked. I was not holding on to Rachel, suddenly thought I had an obligation, somehow, to marry Rachel one day and didn't want to marry her—felt myself falling to pieces—my backbone already in the grass, my head in Aron's hands, legs and arms propped against the walls. My voice said, "More or less, yes, best really when we're talking on the phone." A girl I didn't know burst out laughing, and Rachel drew away from me, her face sallow. Aron repeated, "Time to eat, drink, and dance, ladies and gentlemen. You're coming along, aren't you? No?" Rachel and I stood next to one another, each of our faces covered with a separate bell jar. The girl I hadn't met whispered to me, "You're coming with us." Walking through the darkness again, various parts of various buildings, flickering candles, singing, shouting. "The wedding," said Aron, "is only now about to begin in earnest." How easy and good it felt to be with Aron. With Rachel there was always my uneasiness, my fear that she was expecting me to be the one to create the afternoons and evenings for her, to shape her life, to decide everything. I wanted to stay with my friend and at the same time get acquainted with this new girl, a pretty, sprightly thing. But I knew my obligation was to stay with Rachel, to ask her to forgive me; I had hurt her? Yet as if beaten by a superhuman opponent, I followed the others through the darkness; I couldn't walk upright any longer.

Large hall, long tables, richly and colorfully set for the wedding ceremony; the bright room seemed a bit like the refectory of a monastery. "You're going to stand out there in the dark?" asked Aron. I felt as though there were an impenetrable curtain between inside and out, imagined I wasn't capable of entering the hall where the joyous guests were waiting for the bridal couple. A quick goodbye to Aron and the unknown girl. Without touching her, Aron whispered in Rachel's ear; she shook her head; and already we were walking silently in the direction of the Western Sector—along the outer wall of the Armenian Cemetery, and farther, along the illuminated city wall leading down from Mount Zion toward the Jaffa Gate. We had forgotten to pick up the things we had bought; too late to go back and get them. A warm drizzle was blowing in our faces—in a matter of a single minute, one kind of weather had turned into another. Clouds raced over the full moon. Moths and beetles seemed to be fluttering inside my stomach—Rachel had become untouchable, even the slightest contact with her shoulder now seemed out of the question. If I do not enter the Law, I thought to myself, then I shall remain without any framework, a piece of driftwood in the ocean.

In the New City, Saturday evening was now rampant, despite the drizzle. Hardly has the parting of the Holy Day from the rest of the week been completed, when a totally different life begins; people pour into the streets; shops, snack bars, movie houses open, hunger and restlessness driving vast groups to the same places. Now the buses were running; smell of gasoline again. Metal objects, insects, heavy-sweet smell of flowers. Armed women soldiers among the seeking, rushing, drifting people.

Every point of the compass in my head. The boys and girls, incredibly beautiful, lawless. Nothing is new under the sun? Everything is vanity and a chasing after the wind? Solomon— mightiest ruler in the history of this city— surely King Solomon did not humble himself before the Law, I thought; he cast off the yoke like an old skin.

In the hubbub of Ben Yehuda Street, ten figures were crawling over the wet sidewalk, shrouded from head to foot in coarse brown sackcloth. They stretched out their arms and legs, dragged themselves down the street like casualties of some war. The Saturday evening crowd formed a cordon for them, some of the men kicked at the legs, shoulders, even the shrouded heads of these faceless creatures in fun. Like dying insects, the muffled group scuttled away. Rachel went past them quickly, eyes straight ahead. Past the new building on whose ground floor the private screening had taken place. (War, empty park wet with rain, distant mountain peak on fire. Words are bullets.) I scurried after Rachel like a house pet.

We rode up to the seventh floor, in that narrow, neon-lit cubicle; no touching, no speaking. Looked each other in the eyes, without smiling, without sadness. Every day is a living being. Rachel touched my fingertips. Thoughts many stories high, all at once, like multiple dreams in a short span of time. Rachel held my hand tight. The elevator came to a halt at the top floor. Little apartments are like bird snares. I felt trapped instantly. Without an extended family, without a house, without a garden, no encounter of two people can last. Little boxed-in apartments suffocate "great feelings." As Rachel was filling the tub, very hot (steam was already beginning to pour into the hallway)—it was then I knew: I would never really be able to love anyone but my mother, not in all my life. And certainly never a stranger.

5.

. . . UNFAMILIAR PATH. I am wandering along a stony path. Under my feet are the fir needles. In my hand a lightweight walking stick. It's like an awakening whenever a flashback ends. The interior images give way again to those of the real world outside. I am coming out of the woods, see park benches and trash baskets, wander over to a somewhat higher, sloping field, and scramble over a barbed-wire fence. Without a soul, I wouldn't need any sleep: that's circling around in my head again. But that's certainly no consolation; it doesn't make having to die or having to miss out on

things any easier to bear. If death must come, I am thinking, then let it come when the Flood of Fire is visited upon us. If there is to be a downfall, then let it coincide with the End of Days. No! Even then, let me be counted among the survivors. Allow me to be one of the workers on whatever new construction there may be. I beseech You, do not let me die!

A parklike area, war heroes are buried here, and founders of the State. Eucalyptus trees, white shrubbery. Warm wind, smell of plants, an avenue of pine trees. I am trying to decipher the writing chiseled into a memorial stone. Am I reading it wrong? For what I am reading, from right to left, seems to say: Hiroshilayim, or Hiroshalayim? Yeroshalayim? The smoke is so thick, so sticky, it still covers up any possible glimpse of You. Where are You? You, listen, Almighty, One and Only, Everlasting Being, I love You with all my heart, and with all my soul, and with all my strength. "Hiroshima? Shema Yisrael!" I am standing before the walls of my heart. You put the world into my heart and let me be at home everynowhere. The vectors that are tearing at me—do I want to let them tear at me? He who fears You, are we to listen to his words? I shall lay the cornerstone of my search for You. I must build the gate for my journey into You. Yet if I were to enter into the Law, everything that is my everyday would slide away from me, splinter, burn up. I do not have the courage to lift myself out of this world. Did you create me so that I would take

You as the Truth? If I were to journey into You,
I would never return to the place where the
light dwells in eternal unrest. I still remain
with myself in the everyday, at ground level;
and I cling to it so hard. Why do I cling to it so
hard? I follow the avenue of pines at the foot of
the hill. That is my *foot of the hill, those are*
my *pine trees, I am thinking—my glance*
firmly fixed on the ground. Under my feet is
my arid, wrinkled earth. . . .

6.

MEN AND WOMEN clad in black, packed close
together; a boys' choir in their midst, three-part
chorale. Priests under pointed black cowls
swung their silver censers. The boys' singing
sounded sweet and heavy at the same time.
Standing on tiptoe, I could make out a flower-
decorated coffin in the middle of the gathering.
Rays of sun fell from a skylight into the side
nave of the church, forming a sloping plane of
light. I was looking for Dana; moved through
the packed rows of people closer to the coffin.
The dead man's nose stood out white above the
rest of his face; his cheeks had been rouged.

Even at the Mass for this dead stranger I pitched my tent, stood there mourning with the others, head bowed. Dana, curly black hair and great dark eyes, was leaning against a gleaming blue faience pillar, framed by resplendent silver objects. She was startled when she recognized me, told me with her eyes that I should not come and stand beside her, had to pretend we didn't know each other. The open coffin was now raised up by six men, carried very slowly toward the entrance, and accompanied by the mourners across the yellowish-white squares of the Armenian Quarter to the cemetery on Mount Zion. Dana, a relative of the Armenian Archbishop, and I first met at the opening of a new museum.

It was not until we were slowly leaving the church that I recognized the face of the dead man: the watchman at the gate. Every day he stood at the principal gateway into the Armenian Quarter, a tall silver staff in his hand, standing guard until late in the evening. The black-robed choirboys walked in double file across the shimmering church square, disappeared under stone archways into parts of the city I'd never seen. Dana gestured with a nod of her head in the direction of the main gate: we were to meet outside the quarter.

When I wanted to greet her in a doorway with a hug, she withdrew. I kissed the back of her slender hand, as embarrassed and awkward as a figure skater off balance. In the hot afternoon light we walked in the direction of Jaffa Gate;

we climbed the steps to the city wall, where we could take a walk around most of the Old City and then return. Church bells, a Sunday just before Easter, in the month of Nisan—the bells filled the brilliant air with the sounds of peace. My childhood was full of such calm and quiet: summer holidays, the ridges of the highest Alps, thicket of meadows; how I adored the smell of new-mown hay. Was I, in fact, only longing for its sweetness? Did I feel at home only in places where the smell of fresh hay was to be found? Summer meadows, high mountains, pine forests, church bells—who *am* I without these? We looked down at the two cities; glass-walled apartment complexes and hotels in the one direction, little stone cubes and cupolas, towers, battlements, in the other. I spoke about my longing for the opposite, for mountain villages, waterfalls, freshly cut fields.

"And if you sent me a postcard from there, it would only say that this place—where we're standing now—was your real home," Dana replied. "Do you think you're the only one who knows anything about this yearning and seeking? You may think you're an exception, but most people feel the way you do. Who really knows what country or what city or what intellectual atmosphere they belong in? I was born somewhere else, I grew up somewhere else; do you think I'm not searching, too? But I like wherever I happen to be. And I don't torment myself. When we're together, is your mind on someone else?" We stopped walking. Dana looked unswervingly into my eyes, with a look as if she—hardly older than a schoolgirl—were close to the end of her long life, beyond space and time. From one moment to the next she was capable of enveloping herself in an icy zone of silence. Then she was clothed in inaccessibility, and if I wanted to take hold of this shroud, get a mental fix on Dana, she turned to stone beneath it; my speech was defeated, my tongue lamed. Every time we saw each other it was like meeting for the first time, even if we had seen each other earlier that day. She became incomprehensible, unclassifiable; she would not let me reconnect the things the two of us had previously constructed. She erased all their traces—like those drawing pads: pull out a metal sheet and everything you've written or drawn disappears.

Dana's look gradually grew gentler and more cheerful; I found my tongue again. After such a parching silence, I always felt an obligation to fill with words the empty space that had yawned and threatened to go on and on—and I also felt that Dana expected me to perform this task. I was an electric motor on a test bench. Under Dana's direction, my speech, which had been switched off, was converted into a renewed desire to talk. I told her a dream I had had this Sunday morning: in the moonlight I had come up to the great locked door of a house belonging to relatives of Dana, somewhere in the Alps; in front of it animal embryos cowered, newborn kittens, still wet from the womb. Dana and an unknown girl were sitting on the copper roof, their backs to me. The girl was a sleepwalker, and Dana, wide awake, was trying to bring her out of a trance in which she was fervently praying. I called out "Magdalene!" to the catatonic girl, whereupon she turned around toward me, her eyes wide open, and performed, like a silent medium, the Veneration of the Virgin—so powerfully, so electrically, that it woke me up.

Above a field near the New Gate. As I was speaking, I watched a group of lively lovers down below, in the grass, some of them resting their heads in their partners' laps. Whatever was taking place behind me did not exist for the moment; only if I had turned around would the congested confusion of the Old City have been there again. It is a trick of the imagination that has been with me for as long as I can remember: whatever is behind me, isn't there—comes back to life only when I look around again.

"I *do* have a friend like that," said Dana after a moment of silence, stroked one eyebrow with a fingertip, something she often did. "She was a somnambulist, Elisabeth, even before I met her. We were at a boarding school together in the mountains. . . ." Dana bathed the wanderer in me in a vapor of effortlessness, played badminton, picked lilacs inside me. The cool child, the stony-gentle girl that she was—unviolated and inviolate—made her the focus of my curiosity. The unspoken things that hovered between us beguiled me. The fact that Elisabeth, the figure in my morning dream, really existed, only confused and excited me the more. Dana took it as little more than a slightly surprising natural phenomenon. And then she told me the dream she had dreamed that morning. I had to bend close to her, her voice was so soft. "In the Old City, the noise, the confusion as always, but everything so strange, as if long ago. I wanted to get out, far away; went through the Lions' Gate and kept on straight ahead. It grew quiet, fewer people, fewer houses, no more noise; a great rock; already in the desert; I got inside the rock through a crack; in a cavern lay a covered body—covered with a white cloth. I tugged at the cloth, but the skin—it was sticking to it. I was horrified. I pulled the entire skin off the dead man—until all that was left was a peculiar mass, formless, like rubber that was melting. I raised him up, hugged him tight, but couldn't wake him up. There was just a kind of white light emanating from his solar plexus. Then his legs flopped apart, and I crawled in between them. When I woke up, my face was covered with tears." I believed I knew whom Dana had seen in her dream, but just to be sure asked her who it might have been. With a jolt she stopped walking, stared at me; the words shot out of her with the force of a grown woman's voice, "You *know* who!" I looked at the luxuriant vegetation in rear courtyards and monastery gardens. We stood there silent; the rhythmic scratching of a rake could be heard; it mingled with my keyed-up sense of shame.

A boy came running toward us; I thought I knew who he was. He wore a little black cap, white tassels dangled below his belt. I recognized him with a start; he was the son of a rabbi who taught at my Torah school. Would he tell his father about Dana? "Where is your kipah?" he shouted, still some distance away. He paid no attention to Dana as we greeted each other, looked right through her as if she were a transparent body. I explained that months ago I had given up wearing my kipah after I left the yeshivah in the afternoon. "Why? You don't want people to know?" he asked. Dana smiled strangely; she walked past us and away, with exaggerated strides. "Me, well I'd feel like I was sort of naked," said Ezra, "without my kipah, awful feeling. You planning to marry that one?" He couldn't tell from looking at her that she was a goy, I thought; told him cheerfully I'd be postponing any marriage for a few more years. He shook his head. "She'd be just perfect for you; you're already pretty old and you have to start making children. You hear every day about overpopulation. That's crazy. Half the world hasn't been settled yet; people make *one* child and have three dogs. Marry her, promise me? Wonder what that feels like, without my kipah. . . ." But as soon as he took it off he covered his head with the inside of his elbow. In a second the cap was back in its place. ". . . really feels terrible. I'll never do *that* again!" And off he ran toward Jaffa Gate.

"In buses—but it's just as bad at the university, and even on the street—people look so angry whenever they see the cross," Dana was saying. I had caught up with her. "Hate in their eyes, really, I swear it's true; just as soon as they saw it around my neck, the passengers would move away from me. I took it off a year ago—just gave in. And now, everyone thinks that I'm one of them—my people do, your people do. Same as with you." Same as with me. Smooth-shaven Everynobody caught between the worlds. Dana, one of the knots of my invisible net? Seekers find each other. We are wanderers in a holy sense, I thought, this city is our center—all seeking leads us here. "We're moving in opposite directions, but we keep touching the same midpoint, like the spokes of a wheel," said Dana. "I would so much like you to . . . if only I could feel that you were ready, that you could open yourself up to Him. He gave us His flesh and His blood. One cannot live without Him; He is bread, wine, overflowing joy. He is the love that never ends. All you must do is ask Him to enter your heart. I feel Him in me. Whoever believes in the Son will have eternal life. And whoever does not believe in the Son will never see life. The anger of the Father will weigh him down; haven't you ever read that? No one gets to the Father except through Him. If you're looking for a new life— that's why you came here, isn't it?—then follow *Him*, take Him into your heart, begin today, you don't know how wonderful it is."

My heart was beating violently. I felt the

numbness that invades me whenever things closest to me become the subject of a conversation; the anxiety and anger at not finding the words for a reasonable and effective reply; the profound impotence that causes heat to rise to the surface of my skin from deep inside. I sought language strong enough to blast holes, move cities, and found only splinters, fragments, ruins. I said to Dana that every person is a daughter or a son of the Everlasting, but that no one is more than anyone else. If the Everlasting exists, then He created her and me as His children—to insist that one man alone was His only begotten son was a disgusting oversimplification and disparagement, and Dana's love was tantamount to idolatry. I added that her feelings were the perceptions of her own soul, that she was perceiving a holy fragment of the Everlasting, which was her own Self, whenever she spoke about an "only begotten Son."

"You talk and you talk, but you have no idea of what you're talking about," she interrupted. "I can only pity you, you're so *poor*. The miracle happened two thousand years ago. He was our Savior, but you stand there in the shadow and wait. You really believe that if you follow some rigid law it's more than having his Son, love itself, inside you? He died for your sins, but that has nothing to do with keeping milk and meat apart or worrying about lighting a fire or turning off a light on Saturday. That's all superficial, has nothing to do with feelings. You don't know anything, you can't feel it. He is

Man *and* He is God, can't you manage to understand that? . . . Or do you simply want to trample things and destroy them?"

I couldn't answer, thought of leaving Dana
there upon the city wall, never seeing her again,
but I contained myself, said nothing at first.
Throngs in front of Damascus Gate. I looked
down on the tops of heads, hats, the kaffiyehs of
the Bedouins and pilgrims, saw people selling
bread, bananas, coffee. And at my back (after I
looked around), the Old City of light-yellow
stone, pieced together like sets of boxes, next to
one another, on top of each other, half-dome
roofs, covered by a dense forest of antennas,
cats running back and forth among the metal
trees. As if by magic, a soldier appeared next to
us; he had been on sentry duty, hidden in one of
the embrasures of the wall. "You know what
the worst thing about this whole job is?" he
asked. "Here, take it, heft it. Bet you can't do
that for long." I lifted his machine gun—very
heavy, no question of it; gave it back to him
right away. "Know what I'd like to do, what I
really always want to do? Shoot at that dome,
it's just the right distance away." He pointed
with the gun barrel at the yellow cupola of the
Dome of the Rock—odd how small it looked
from where we were standing, even though it
still dominated the whole view. Instead of letting fly at the armed guard, cursing him for his
stupid insolence, I just stood next to him, staring at the ground, smiling feebly.

Under the hot light of day. We walked along

the city walls, in the direction of Herod's Gate. The colors of the city, green and ocher. In wide ellipses, the other tints and hues encircled these two key colors. We did not speak. Dana and I had been marching along, one behind the other, for some time, like strangers, until Dana stopped, turned around to me. "You're trying to conceal your arrogance, but you're not succeeding." We continued along, I didn't answer her, thought: in spite of all my protestations, I do consider myself one of the elect. Don't I feel pride in being part of a people of priests, a light to the nations? Did HaShem not speak to me alone and to my race; did He not give the Torah to us alone, on Mount Sinai, entrust us alone to keep His word, to guard His word, until the advent of the Age of the Messiah, until the birth of a man who is to come from our very midst? Was I not also one of those who believed that one day the nations of the earth would flock to us, in the Age of Messiah, begging to be allowed to study Torah. Was I not also one who believed we were chosen to prepare humanity for that Kingdom to come, to call out anew every day, for millennia, "No, Messiah has not yet come! No, Messiah has not yet come! No, Messiah has not yet come!" And simultaneously the very opposite in my head: I cannot believe that on this whole earth only Torah is absolute truth. Both forces equally strong in me: the glowing pride, and the doubt that knows.

I lied to her, swore that I wasn't governed by arrogance but by the feeling of being different, not better, not worse, than others. Every people was given its own task to fulfill, I said, Dana's people a different one from mine. "What cold language you have," she replied. "When you write, is your language just as ice-cold? You *are* arrogant. And you wonder why people hate you all? You must read more carefully what is written in your books: you shall destroy all whom I, your Lord, shall deliver to you—something very much like that. You shall not spare them—no one will rise up against you—until you have exterminated them all. But the most selfless, the most luminous, the kindest thing that has ever appeared on this earth, *that* you wish to degrade. Perhaps you don't know that one of your Commandments says you must drive the idolaters from your land, and in your eyes that is who we are, those are my brothers and sisters, my parents, all my relatives; you've already begun to drive out those of different faiths, but it will not really begin in earnest—I know that—until your King is born and the Third Temple is standing. Well, first the Dome of the Rock will be demolished—right?—and your Temple will be erected again on the same spot, and then you'll go out hunting for us, because we . . . we'll keep faith with the Savior. His is the Kingdom and the Power and the Glory, forever."

She had spoken quietly, her features remained friendly. I knew that any quick retort would be a brutal wound in our encounter. I stuttered something imprecise, quoted some passages, something about reconciliation, and thought at the same time: didn't the Circumcised One swear never to extinguish a single letter of the Law? Didn't he himself keep holy six hundred and thirteen commandments; didn't he pray at the fixed hours *Shema Yisrael, Adonai Eloheinu, Adonai Ehad*, the prayer at the very heart of Israel to this day? Didn't he draw all his knowledge and deeds from the Books of the Torah, himself a scribe and pupil of the excellent Pharisees? Were not his disciples and the zealots who followed him the ones who cast him, the Simple Prophet, in the light he would never have claimed for himself? And simultaneous with this chain of thought, the very opposite in my head. I had lost the core of what I possessed, lost my center, as if it had flowed out of a hole in my head onto the stones of the wall. What remained was the tormenting question to myself: do not my people live in enmity toward everything luminous and easeful; aren't they barbarically, intolerantly set against the slightest suggestion of fulfillment and salvation? On their banners was not modesty, humility, and discretion but aggressiveness, provocation, and arrogance. Am I not, too, an obtrusive, pushy man, loud and without inner dignity? Jacob, I am your descendant; you lied to your father on his deathbed, betrayed your only brother. I fit instantly into any surroundings, accommodate myself at once to any set of expectations and conditions. I know nothing of the sedentary, hearth and home; I am not prepared to put my life at stake for any cause. I lack toughness, I lack gentleness. I shall disavow my forefathers. I don't need history as part of my biography. I shall cut myself off from Yehuda Mordechai Cassuto and his tribe, from the Roccamoras, and Suschitzkys, from the Bravos and Hirschlers. I'm not defined by the past but by the future. May these progenitors no longer live within me, the mothers and fathers. I tear asunder the bond of blood, it no longer exists, let me go. I deny you. You're not the salt of the earth; you're the scum of the earth. I beseech you, cast me out.

Dana's voice filtered through my thoughts. It assumed shapes—my fear as a child of the underside of automobiles. Avenues of chestnut trees, racing horses, ringtoss. I thought: did I seek them out, my parents, before my birth? Was Dana calling, "Come back"? My story was a no-roof-over-my-head story. I am a slave of freedom. "Come back. Where are you? Where are you?" Words are bullets. Elevators, always nothing but elevators. Pater Noster. "Where are you? Forgive me, was that all so serious for you? Forgive me. Can you hear me?" Felt Dana's arm pressed against my arm, Dana snuggling up to me, a touching monument: Young Man as Gazelle, Artist-Clown. She lay her head on my shoulder, kissed my neck. We kissed each other—a deep kiss, breathlessness; from my solar plexus a sensual thrill radiated into the network of my capillaries. I was totally in Dana's hands. Devising a way to continue our walk again, without ropes, without a net, seemed to present an insurmountable obstacle.

Next to a playing field in the Old City. It smelled of dry earth and gasoline; the colors of the field green and ocher; children were playing soccer, playing acrobat in the tall jungle gyms. My gaze was directed at the boys' earlobes, the scars on their soccer balls, traces of rust on the goalposts, while I tried to cut myself free from Dana's heart and hands.

Past stone-paved courtyards and little vegetable gardens. We stumbled over bits of rubble fallen from the city wall, made our way through a thicket of underbrush. Yellow-golden light on the city as we approached Herod's Gate. In my lower arms, in my chest and thighs, exhaustion. But Dana looked brighter and fresher than she had at the start of our walk around the city, shed her own rays on the afternoon light, young blood, niece of the archbishop. The air smelled of honey and stone. I felt as if I were being poured into the growing twilight, into the lassitude of the sky; the air, the weather, surrounded me, warm and heavy. There are kinds of light that, like odors, awaken memories. There are days on which the light shows us the way a century long ago must have looked. There are evenings on which the growing twilight spans a bridge of glass back to an evening in my early childhood. I saw the final rays of this day's sun projected on the Mount of Olives as if on a wide screen, mixture of red and brown gold. What a feeling of exaltation, I thought, to be permitted a space of time on this earth and then to leave it again, the way we leave a room. Sometimes when I was with Dana I suddenly said things that would never have occurred to me in Rachel's presence. Dana drew from me a way of speaking thoughts that were usually altogether foreign to my nature. To step into the world, and after a time then to die, I said, was like entering a room and then leaving it. "Since I was a child," Dana said, "I have been living in a plant-room; quite incredible to have something like that, in my head, in my thoughts, to be able to create such a room for myself. There I live, in a forest somewhere, perhaps in Graubünden, in the Alps, all alone; the carpet is a meadow, the sky my roof, the fir trees the walls. That's where I'll go to live when the war, or any great catastrophe, comes. Then I'll move into my greenroom."

Old bread, lamb bones, transistor batteries; on the other side, aroma of honey cakes from little bakeries. We walked out into the Eastern Sector. Silvery evening, rapid transition from day to night, here in my world's midpoint. Dana wanted to introduce me to friends of hers who kept a shop in Salah-ed-Din Street not far from the American Colony Hotel. With Dana in the Eastern Sector—how different from being with Rachel. Dana was at home here, not merely an occupant of her own quarter; she came over here every day to go shopping, to meet friends, to go to a film. With her beside me, the Western Sector seemed like some distant foreign enclave. Suddenly I recognized Mendel on the other side of the street, striding along on some errand; what had brought him here, to "enemy territory"? Mendel, Aron's younger brother, always dressed in black, with a white shirt, a large hat, the only way I ever saw him dressed. Fringes dangled at his waist, twisted wool threads that the strictly Orthodox wear at the four corners of their undershirts, since it is written: you shall make for yourself tassels on the four corners of your cloak, as a reminder at all times of the six hundred and thirteen commandments; *tzitzit* as a visible admonition not to follow your heart, your eyes, but to take HaShem's Torah upon yourself as a yoke—a memorial, these tassels, to protect you in your traffic with the secular world. (How should I enter the Law, if even outer signs like these set impossible barriers between me and my struggle to take the yoke upon myself?) I became flushed as Mendel stood beside us. I would have to introduce Dana and give him an explanation. "I'm on my way to prayer, really in a hurry," he interrupted me, "but first I have to speak to you, right now." He lived in a very strict Talmud and Torah school. A short time before, I had met Daniel, a young bookdealer, taken a room in his apartment so that I might have a home, on the days when I was not living with Rachel—and Mendel worshiped Daniel's sister Leah, got to know her through Aron and me. Although he was strictly forbidden any contact with the world outside, he often broke

away, told them that he was going to visit relatives, but actually would pick up Leah at her
school and walk home with her, did it again and
again. "Come on! Don't just stand there; who
can tell who might be watching us." He tugged
at my sleeve, paying no attention at all to Dana,
or so I thought; she was nothing but air for all
he seemed to care—or some servant of mine.
While he was tugging my shirt, Dana wrote
down the address of her friends for me, slipped
it into my hand and disappeared into the throng
of citizens of the Other City.

"Who was that, anyhow? Your cousin? You
look a little alike, where is she from?" He
pulled me into a barbershop, no customers—
past some old green leather armchairs. "Quick,
into the back room, it was crazy standing
around so long out there with you; they're spy-
ing on me everywhere. You have to help me, I
need your advice." The shop owner came into
the back room, a small, haggard man, dark skin,
black eyes. Mendel exchanged a few rapid sentences with him in that language so abomi-
nated by those who live in the Other City:
Mendel and I the army of occupation, except we
carried no weapons over our shoulders. The barber retreated, insulted. Now Mendel began to
arrange what was on his mind, spoke with a
calmer voice. "You can see that I'm pale, that
I'm upset, fine—I'm waging world war inside
me; they've found out that I'm seeing Leah. So
now it's been arranged for me to study with the
best rabbi I ever met, even supposed to live

with him—you couldn't imagine a greater honor. But under what conditions? Only one: never see Leah again, do you understand? So what should I do now? I've already howled, wept on the telephone with her; I told her the story. And she? She won't help me. Nobody will help me, you understand that? Which world should I choose?" The barber looked in; he countered the invasion with the only weapon he was allowed to have, the only one they hadn't taken from him: the look in his eyes. Mendel went on without paying any attention to him. "I was with her today, paced back and forth so much I rumpled up all the carpets in her place. I'm not even allowed to call her up now. What should I do, what's your advice? I can tell from looking at you that you don't have an answer, what's wrong with you anyhow, you're acting like a stranger today, well, in any case I'm in the middle of a whirlwind, do you understand? So do me one favor now: first, you'll leave before I do; if they recognize you, I'm in danger, you're not even wearing a kipah, so they'll know right away: he's the go-between. By the way, why don't you ever wear the kipah anymore? You don't want to be recognized for what you are? You want to be liked by the goyim, is that it? Anyhow, you go first, I'll leave three minutes later. Please give Leah a hug for me, in case you see her—at least you can do that for me. Here comes that guy again—yes, yes, we're going now, disgusting bastard. And you—thanks—sometimes we just have to pour out our hearts, please understand; and hug my dear Leah for me, and don't look back when you leave here—forgive me, I'm so upset. So then, my friend." Squeezing past the owner, I left the barbershop, could see him out of the corner of my eye sharpening his razor on a leather strop. I felt hostility toward Mendel's capacity for such emotion. I envied him from the depth of my heart for the advantage he had over me in that very regard—for the emotion I thought I would never be capable of in this life.

Next to a brilliantly lit movie house I found the camera store owned by Dana's friends. Their faith prescribed Friday as a day of rest and so they stayed open Sundays. Dana was sitting on a desk, bent slightly forward with her legs tucked up. On the walls, photographs of the city: Temple Mount, Church of the Holy Sepulcher, Mount of Olives, Mount Scopus; no picture of the Western Wall. The brothers' names were Raphi and Mahmoud. Raphi left the room as soon as I came in. I sat down in an orange armchair, sank into it. The three of us didn't speak, didn't move. The only thing in the room was the sound of the television, some documentary about refugees who had left their home after a war, drifting around like splinters of wood on the high seas. Only a few of them could be rescued by a freighter crew. I wanted to leave the store. Dana sat silently on the desk, smiling at Mahmoud, and then he turned to me. "Are you wondering why my brother left the shop when you came in? It took him two hours today to get to our mother's place. It is only fifteen minutes to Ramallah, but never have we made it there in fifteen minutes, because we must take off all our clothes behind the bushes, at the checkpoint. . . . I've seen documents, by the way, that prove that none of the things happened the way you insist they happened. You with your 'alleged' program of extinction. And you use these fairy tales of yours as an excuse to mistreat us, to murder us. You are always complaining, 'I am so poor! I am so miserable!' and you cut down our lemon groves and you trample on our gardens. Like three thousand years ago—you took our land from us, then, too. You tried to destroy us, then, too. We are Canaanites, do you understand that; I am a Canaanite—nothing has happened to make that any different. Now, you have returned; but you remain strangers in our land. Where the house of my parents once stood now there is a big apartment building for your immigrants from all over the world. My oldest brother, he has been in prison because he 'reacted' when that happened. Believe me, we want to live in peace with you, but for that we must divide the country between us, and most of all we must divide this *city* between us— al-Quds it is, our Holy City. Until that happens, there will be no peace. That I can swear to you. You will see for yourself, when I go with you—they will stop me, search me; you will see that very soon."

Mahmoud did not wait for me to reply; he

spoke with Dana. Taste of impotence in my mouth. Another freighter, another rescue of castaways nearly dead from starvation. A feeling as if my body were covered with filth. Were the encounters, the experiences today, a way of forcing me to throw out anchor, finally—to pitch an emergency tent in my quest for *some* place where I might belong? Kinsman of my forebears: had I come as occupier into this camera store? Had my blood relationship made me Mahmoud's ancient adversary, his sworn enemy from the beginning of time? Made him my foe and hater? *If any harm follows, then you shall give life for life, eye for eye, tooth for tooth, hand for hand, foot for foot, burn for burn, wound for wound, stripe for stripe.* Is that the way it is to continue until the coming of the Messiah? Dana and Mahmoud were laughing, consciously avoiding my eyes. I stared at the television image: a spinal tap was being taken from one of the rescued children; the little boy shrieked in pain as if he were being burned alive. I'd never seen anything like it before—a needle simply stuck into his marrow, through skin and spine . . . and at that instant, the image vanished to a pinpoint of light and the neon lights in the room, the lights in the street went out. Before I could figure out what had happened, I thought: I must examine each part of the world in rapid succession before they are blotted out, in the "great catastrophe." Mahmoud was groping around in drawers, cabinets, glass showcases, looking for a candle.

The darkness built a framework for the chaos inside me. We were walking in the direction of the Damascus Gate; the blackout had affected the entire city; as far as we could see not a single electric light was burning. A large lamp store: pitch-dark, the house of light cowered under the night sky. We walked past a parked army jeep; tall antennas stuck from its hood and rear; two young men were sitting in it, motionless. When we came alongside it, one of them threw his door open, blocking Mahmoud's path. The second one was instantly beside him; I saw the gleam of brass cartridges on his ammunition belt. They shined their flashlights directly into Mahmoud's eyes. No one said a word. Mahmoud produced a crumpled ID, then the soldiers grabbed his arms, shoved him against a building; he had to place his hands against the stone wall above his head; they frisked him: sleeves, pockets, trousers, over and over; they also felt several times between his legs. (Those who were once the persecuted have become the persecutors that they not be persecuted again.) And while my brothers were nailing the stranger to the Cross, I was determined to go up to them, curse them, command them in a voice of authority to let Mahmoud go at once. And didn't move a muscle, let them be—even when they motioned him to get into the patrol car. Dana was frozen to the spot; she remained as mute as Mahmoud and the soldiers. The darkness of the night and the silence of this interlude were one—until the motor started up, the powerful headlights flooded the street with their piercing beams, and the car jerked forward with a squeal of tires (Mahmoud did not look back at us), disappearing into the darkness of the Eastern Sector.

A blockade had been set up around an empty warehouse: bomb scare near the Damascus Gate. In a wedge of light, a robot, set in motion by remote control, a device no taller than a man, six arms, made its way into the building—headless knight, it rolled on invisible wheels into the bowels of the warehouse, fired off several muffled shots there . . . silence . . . and the little tank slowly rolled out again. The barricades were removed, floodlights extinguished, all clear given, the machine hoisted back onto the bed of an army truck. Surrounded by darkness. Dana wanted to tell her uncle the archbishop about Mahmoud's arrest, thinking he might be able to arrange for an immediate release. She held me partially responsible for what had happened. I felt that my failure to intervene had disappointed her, had even made her contemptuous of me—but she didn't express a syllable of this, in words. She was capable as it was of controlling the way I felt, the way I behaved, by means of her subtle shifts. I relapsed into my anxiety. I thought, is Dana really the exceptional case I thought her to be, or simply someone with a certain lack of compassion? Her silence was impenetrable, her distance and estrangement annoyed me, seemed an affectation, at least from this altered point of view. But what power was it she had that enabled her to buckle this belt of silence so tightly? Double mimosa, raised in a petrifying chill, trapped under bell jars. We crossed through the murky Old City, all the roller blinds down, odors lingering in the souks. The walls of the Church of the Sepulcher were bathed in electric light, even the nearby streetlights were working: an oasis of electricity, the church was independent of the State power system. At the unguarded main entrance to the Armenian Quarter, we stood under a cypress; I searched for words to say in parting from this hard-headed girl. In a schoolyard nearby, children were playing despite, or probably because of, the prevailing darkness. I leaned against the trunk of the tree; its upper branches swayed in the breeze. A feeling of having a home, after a walk has come full circle—I basked in this sentiment for minutes on end.

We took leave without speaking, touched hands, touched shoulders. Suddenly, Bishop Narkissian was standing there; Dana was startled; he had appeared as if from a theater pit. I knew him slightly, saw his gray goatee in the pale night light, round spectacles, snaggled teeth. He was dressed in black silk vestments, head covered by a high, pointed cowl. He placed his hand on my shoulder, its warmth penetrating my shirt. Dana was speaking with Narkissian in a dream language. (Armenian words sound a little like a made-up language I invented and used as a child.) As the bishop was listening to Dana's agitated account of the event, he gripped my shoulder harder, was already beginning to hurt me—Narkissian's reaction was transferred to the sinews and muscles of his powerful hand. I didn't dare to shake it off.

Candles were burning in the stone vaults. The long, cool corridors of the monastery building reverberated with the sound of our footsteps. Narkissian led me to his cell. Dana said she would return as soon as she had told her family what had happened. In the darkness, the bishop removed his silk cape; it rustled like paper. Then he lighted oil lamps and candles, which filled the room with a soft glow. "Come closer to me, over here," he urged. "You'll be able to see better; sit next to me." He was dressed now in a blue robe that hung to his ankles. I looked around in the stone chamber: on the walls, pictures of dead patriarchs, painted icons, and photographs of Armenian churches, curving constructions on rocky promontories in the midst of a wild landscape of steppes. Among them were group photographs of his relatives, emigrated from the homeland, scattered for generations, persecuted, humbled, at times resurrected, only to be enslaved once again, yet never obliterated, a stateless people filled with the unshakable power to survive. A papier-mâché model of the Church of the Holy Cross stood on a writing table. "It is on the Island of Aghtamar, in Lake Sevan—do you like it? I've just come from there. Please, come, sit down."

He sat on an upholstered bench, had poured us each a glass of sweet vermouth. There was a knock at the door; Dana entered, crouched into an armchair, leafed quietly through a book with colored illustrations of medieval mosaics. Even in this cell, a foothold has been established for me, I thought: it's rather like a room in a church tower that I once lived in; it's rather like a monastery near the highest peak of the Alps that I once lived in; rather like many splintered fragments of home, scattered over three continents, which offered me a place for my roots but never held on to me, never let me come to rest. But this time I had become a convert; I had been promoted to the post of counsel to the archbishop; Dana and I lived in splendor, waited on by servants, and wherever we traveled, the princely household would accompany us and our five children—all in all, a healthy and intelligent brood. My past and my restlessness extinguished, I had found a way to myself, I had found home, after a thirty years' quest.

"Do you know what your brethren do to me when I walk through their quarter?" asked Narkissian, waking me from my reverie. "Frequently happens that they spit at me, gobs of sticky spittle on my vestments, or on my hood, even sometimes right in my face. You don't believe that, do you? They not only spit, they also stamp on the ground when they see me; that's the way they avoid being infected by my unclean spirit. But you're quite different. Are you really sure both your parents—I mean, you're so—you know what I mean. Come, my friend, give me your hand; so, that's good, what handsome hands. Oh, we know so very little. Have we met in a former life? Why do you take your hand away, my young friend?" I was blushing, looked over at Dana—she was now sitting bolt upright on the edge of the chair, perched on the very edge. Narkissian seemed unconcerned about her, spoke to me about the Island of Aghtamar, about twilight, about table lamps, about summer lightning and an old mounted collection of night-flying moths—but I was looking at Dana's baggy red pants, heavy raw silk, looked at her high-button black blouse, wanted to be with her, wanted to embrace my luminous friend. "This afternoon I was watching you, how upset you were at seeing our Harout dead, our gatekeeper," Narkissian went on. "Do you think that I, pious man that I am, am not afraid of dying? Oh, yes, I am. Fear and horror; oh, God, how afraid I am. What *happens* to us then? I know no more than you do. I'm afraid, from the time I wake till the time I fall asleep. Come, give me your beautiful hand. Would you like a drop more? Please, here, help yourself—candy; won't you stay here with me? No? Do you know that the gatekeeper died in my arms—I can't shake off the feeling. I'll fix a bed for you, with fresh linen, here, next to me— come closer, why are you moving away?"

I got up, had already concocted an excuse: some people were expecting me for dinner, I was already late, and there was no telephone at their place. I assured the bishop of my desire to continue our conversation on one of the following days. I was again incapable of simply putting an end to something with a bold stroke, of cutting anything off. Taken aback by my sudden determination to leave, Narkissian automatically extended his hand to me; I bowed, felt slightly off balance, and stepped back, without turning around. Dana remained in her chair without moving, didn't look at me. I ran through the vaulted corridors, past flickering candles. In the fresh air I walked through the empty squares and streets of the quarter; arrived at the unguarded gateway; it was no longer open, must have been closed and locked in the meantime. Out of breath and sweating, walled into the Other World, I saw the day that was now over flicker past me in reverse; floodlights, Mahmoud, Mendel, city walls, Mass for the dead—a day that had squeezed me, put me in a dungeon: my dungeon keeper my own kinship. I was penned in and given freedom, both at once. This day had wanted to make me come clean, to admit for whom I was prepared to suffer, fight, die, if I had to. This day had fastened reins to my bridle for the first time; I could feel the bit in my teeth. I was pulled up short; and given free rein, and pulled up, and given free rein again—at the walled-in outlet.

Through the thick wooden center door of the gate I could hear voices chattering; I beat with both my fists on the door—it didn't occur to me to return to Narkissian or to Dana. I hammered against the wood, called out *"Hatzilu!"*—couldn't understand how I knew the word for help: *Hatzilu*—and after a few seconds, an answer; shouts; questions I couldn't comprehend; and then the sound of a key in the lock, the anticipated surprise. One wing of the gate swung open, four soldiers were standing there. One of them was holding a massive ring of pass-keys in his hand; I had to tell him all about how I had gotten into this predicament. But then the interrogation quickly merged into general speculation on the possible causes and effects of the blackout. It took a while before I realized that two of the soldiers were young women; one was called Yardena, the other Zahava. Yardena quoted a passage from Psalms she had memorized, then translated it for me: "They know not, nor do they understand; they walk on in darkness; all the foundations of the earth are shaken." My liberators were just about to close the heavy door again, when we could hear footsteps approaching—Dana was holding a very large and heavy key in her hand; the soldiers were laughing; I didn't really know why they were laughing; we all shook hands, said good-bye, then they marched away, back into the ever-present moment of preparing for the next war. Yardena turned around one final time, waved at us. I caught myself in time from shouting to her that we were kinsmen, that I wasn't tied to Dana. I was even thinking of running after them, of explaining to Yardena that I belonged to her, but the four were marching quickly away—I would never be able to catch up to them. Dana was holding something else in her hand; she asked me to touch it. A ring, perfectly plain. She wanted to entrust me with this heirloom, she said; it wasn't to be thought of as a present, but as a kind of loan I could keep until we saw each other next time. I took the ring, thought: I have to accept it; hugged Dana, kissed both her cheeks. ". . . as if I were a molecule that had to detach itself from another molecule. Or, as in the microcosm, elementary particles that are pulling away from each other," she said. "After that, we each live in our own skins again." I hugged her even tighter, didn't want to see her again; and Dana, all at once like something gentle and fluid, calm and tender, blew me a kiss, waved then, closed the gate. I heard the key turn in the lock, the bolt shot twice into its socket. Dana's steps echoed away; I could hear them through the massive gates. After that: silence in darkness. Whatever was behind me didn't exist. I, between nothing and no one. Yet for the first time, I felt reins tugging against my teeth.

7.

. . . BEHIND ME *the avenue of pines, next to me a red metal sculpture, a big traffic intersection ahead of me: I've arrived at the highest point of the hill. View of the city from the rear: to the west, tree-covered mountains, central hospital, reservoir, purification system, power plant, settlements on the outskirts—here is where the city pushes out into the desert. I feel one of the projections of the sculpture with my fingertips, the metal hot from the sun; it smells the way my room did when I was a child. The heat a viscous weight on my skin. I jog across the four-lane road, in my hand the walking stick. I march along for a while toward the south; at the edge of the housing settlement Beit Vegan, tall roadblocks have been set up. If the inhabitants were to see someone driving a car here today, they would try to stone the unfortunate deviant—first destroy the metal frame, then the human frame, with their rocks. To those living in this quarter the mere turning of a key in the ignition, the starting up, the driving of an automobile is the same as making fire—and fire-making one of the basic activities forbidden on New Year's Day. Yesterday I was standing in a synagogue in the New City, heard the blowing of the shofar for the first time in my life, the call for return to the Law, a sound that enters one's very bones. A ram's horn is blown—the same three notes over and over: a pure, a broken, and then another pure note. The first of them focuses the inner vectors, our dissipated strength, to a single point; the broken note rouses us to action, moves us to fill ourselves with the rock-shattering thought: HaShem; the final pure note collects the fragments of our ruin, assembles our now disentangled spirit for a move in the One True Direction. . . . From the windows not a sound of a single radio, no television set turned on, no record player, no kitchen appliance, no typewriter. No one is playing a musical instrument. Wonderful peace and calm. A cat runs past the wall of a house; a half-dead bird dangles from its mouth, wings still beating feebly. At the entrance to a synagogue a bearded young man is standing; under his black robe I see his tzitzit—why is he staring at me? Is he thinking: You, HaShem, are displeased by that gaudy clothing? Is he looking at me so reprovingly because my head is uncovered? I have a little kipah with me; I put it on. (A feeling rushes through me, from my scalp to the soles of my feet—the feeling of belonging.) From the interior, loud praying—half chant, half lamentation. You desire us to make* for ourselves fringes, at the corners of our clothing? You desire us every morning to bind to our arm, to our brow, a cube-shaped receptable? On the Sabbath we may not cross over the boundaries of the city? It doesn't occur to me to separate milk from meat; I can't live that way. You desire us to sacrifice strong and healthy animals when the Temple one day shall be rebuilt? To spray the altar with the blood of a slaughtered beast? To stone a sinner, strangle him, incinerate him, or cut off his head? Is that what You spoke to Moshe Rabeinu when You made the covenant with us? Did You make that covenant with us? I tear the kipah from my head, stick it back in my pocket.

"Hey!"—at my back. I know the shout is meant for me, pretend I don't hear it. (Being shouted at like that is like being awakened in the middle of the night.) The loud cry a second time, a third time: "Hey!" I turn around; an old man is standing there; I don't like him the minute I see him. Yet I imagine that You desire me to approach him. He beckons to me. His black clothing looks worn and threadbare, his big hat misshapen, brim crumpled. The stranger smells of fish, sweet and sour. I think the smell is in his reddish-gray beard. He lays a hand on my shoulder; I feel its warmth through my shirt. "I know, I know everything you are thinking, I know you, I see what is going on in your little head," he says, his voice dancing. "By next Sabbath you'll still be here;

· 114 ·

you won't take that trip you're planning; you'll be coming to my house, you see. I live in Bnei Brak, in Tel Aviv, forty-four Rabbi Akiba Street—remember that—opposite the cigarette factory. You've got a lot more to learn, my child. They're all liars and deceivers, the damned professors at the universities, all dead weights, Professor Monkey and Professor Donkey; they're beasts on two legs; they're turning your brain into a heap of garbage."

His face is already so close to mine that the hairs of my eyebrows are touching his beard. I don't want to jump back for fear of offending him, so we remain that way, head to head. I want to get away from him—yet don't make a move. How can he possibly know anything about my travel plans? How? I ask him where he gets the idea that I'm planning to go away. "I'll teach you everything you must know, my child. In life you need a path to follow, otherwise you're nothing more than a piece of driftwood in the ocean. In life everything is a test, or a punishment, or a reward. You see, if nothing were to come after our life here, then we wouldn't have to die—you'll get to understand all of that well; you're a bright fellow. We'll see each other, in five days: Rabbi Akiba Street, forty-four. . . ." He kisses me firmly on both cheeks, goes to a house entrance, turns around and waves at me. Free from his clutches, good to be rid of him. But his words: I don't want to brush them off; they form a kind of shell for me, for the rest of my walk. How could he possibly know about my travel plans?

These streets You are leading me through—I know them from my dreams. The anxiety You are causing me, electric anxiety, rests easy on my brow. There are fractions of seconds in which You let me know whatever there is to know; it bursts into flame; by the time I reach for it, it has long since disappeared. You turn my head to the side, show me views of Your city among its gardens, its hills, its pointed towers, roofs of its tall buildings, its rounded domes. The yearning my mothers and fathers felt for Your dwelling place—you make it surge up inside me. By the waters of Babylon, there we sat and wept when we remembered Zion. You desire me to break out in sobs, from gratitude? We have returned, to the midpoint of the world. Every adventure sheds its leaves, but not Your city; it is the final splendor on earth. I have returned, to occupy the home, and I begin to realize that it belongs to no one but Yourself. Steep descent, a wide concrete road, away from the settlement in a great curve, down to broad fields of broken stone. Do You see me? The path leads past empty soccer fields; in the city there is still sunlight; here in the stone valley the shadows are already cool; I scramble over boulders in the gravel desert. Do You see me? I beseech You: give me a sign, give me something to hold on to! A tangible sign! Do You hear me? I am lost from Your view, a nothing before Your countenance. You know no more *about me than I about You. Why did You not tell Moshe Rabeinu that the earth was round, that the planets circle the sun? How many lives might You have saved with that one sentence; why did You make known nothing of these realities?*

Why did You permit what happened to my kinsmen, forty years ago?

Because You do not exist.

You do not exist.

"He does not exist!" I shout aloud.

Forgive me, HaShem; look, I fall to my knees, hurt one of them on purpose on the edge of a sharp stone. I remain on my knees before You. In my heart I cry, "Answer me! Answer!" I have been on a journey into the world of anxiety ever since You drew me from the womb, without a shore, without an anchor. You let me be at home nowhere. I have moved away from the house of my father, for You have not given me a fatherland. Have You ever blessed me? Ever cursed my enemies? I am the water, I must pitch my tent in the waves.

I see dark beetles crawling over the cooled ground. Adonai. Let me find a sign at the next street crossing, I beseech You—a piece of bread, an empty wine bottle, a matchbox, yes, that. I am tempting You, despiser of man, let me find a matchbox at the next intersection. And I cross the desert of rubble, in my hand the walking stick, beneath my feet the crunching of stone. . . .

8.

I WOULD OFTEN SIT in the great lobby of the King David Hotel, read the newspapers and magazines, make appointments to meet people there, study the kinsmen who were strangers to me, who had arrived here from the lands of their birth. Between revolving door and broad terrace, between restaurant and coffee shop— there was a place to feel at home; porters and errand boys, elevator operators and waitresses, my homemates; the transients our guests, visitors to my city. In a park behind the wide brick building, I walked among palm trees, plane trees and cactus in bloom, past the swimming pool where children played and young women lay in the sun, their eyelids closed.

On a Friday afternoon in the month of Elul, a few weeks before the New Year's Feast of Rosh Hashanah, I entered the lobby after a walk in the park, bought the Sabbath edition of a great daily paper, watched my guests telephoning, telegraphing, departing, arriving. It was like the belly of an old ocean liner minutes after the anchors had been lowered and she had docked. I saw relatives greeting each other after a long separation, embraces so impassioned, as if life lasted only half the short time it does. I walked back and forth in this busy foyer, close to the groups of travelers. " . . . everything so dark, so brown in the streetcar compartment; tried to keep from crying; had to," said a woman's voice. And a second voice: "Yes, the things that could never happen, have happened, in this century." "Is that paper?" "Is that your handwriting?" "Every people has its guardian angel—except for us; because the Almighty Himself watches over us—or so I once believed." "Us? At home? Television? Never! My husband always says, that's as if you had a goy twenty-four hours a day with you in your house." "I was just about to have Chaim, and somebody comes into the store; he wants to weigh this huge carp he just caught, puts it on the scales, and I had to hold on to the tail for him, and all at once it gives a flip, still a little life in the thing, what a scare that gave me, terrible. And Chaim—day after tomorrow he's thirty years old; never would he eat a fish I fixed for him, never even touched fish."

Two ladies in gossamer silk dresses, covered with massive jewelry, holding on to each other, their fingers intertwined; one of them asked if she might have a look at my newspaper. "Only the headlines," she said. I handed her the thick evening paper. They were reading the headlines to each other—one minute, two minutes—when suddenly a figure attacked me from behind, calling out the name "Pinkas!" as he leapt. I was startled; the ladies let out little shrieks of alarm. I found myself looking into a pair of wide-open, alert eyes: a slender boy was standing before me. Tousled, a bit flushed, but without a particle of fear, he looked up at me. A girl in a yellow uniform asked him, "Are you a guest of the hotel? Where do you live, my funny little friend?" and his great eyes grew calm, became part of an astonished smile; his skin translucent, blue veins shown through his delicately chiseled cheeks. "You're not Pinkas at all," he said with a raspy adolescent voice. "I thought you were my cousin, because maybe he's coming to see us soon—please forgive me." And he laughed gently, straightened his kipah—it was a transformation like a cloudless sky, pure, cool air, after a sudden summer storm. I felt as if I knew him intimately—I looked almost exactly like him once, or so I imagined. Softly he said, "I watch people watching other people, I study them when they are studying each other. Sometimes I speak to them, ask them questions; you do the same thing, don't you?" I nodded; I was calm again; the boy simply stood there beside me; an amorphous sense of security. The features of his face were like filigree work; brown eyes, fragile body, he only came up to my shoulder. He wore a white shirt and black trousers, wore the fringes at his waist. "These lost souls are only here on a visit—I tell them they ought to stay here," he continued, "because they belong here, the way my parents came, and now we have made a home here—*Baruch HaShem*." I wanted to keep him with me. Embarrassed, I asked him what his name was. I felt slightly feverish. "Wanting to do everything at the same time is doing nothing at all, it robs you of your strength," he said. "I observe the Law, and I do it not only because it is pleasing to HaShem, but to keep my soul from cracking; every little slip puts a scratch on the crystal. Are you going to come with me? Will you tell me what it is you tremble for in life and why you do what you do?" As he spoke his whole body was in motion, and his voice seemed to produce little round volleys like the concentric ripples when a stone falls into the water. I wanted him to guide me. The ladies went on reading my newspaper. "Are you always so quiet?" he asked. "You're much too thin for someone your age, and those sunken eyes, and so pale. You've got to get some strength back. You never wear a kipah? Or don't you want to be recognized? It's to stop you from becoming arrogant—that's what it's for. I have to go now, the light is fading. Sabbath will begin very soon."

Shortly after sunset—automobiles were blowing their horns at us, the waxing moon was high in the sky. We walked through a street named Abraham Lincoln; nearby was a soccer stadium, and the cool smells of shrubbery and stone. "You don't have brothers or sisters, right?"

"How can you know that?"

"From looking at you," he said. "I'm an only child, too; but my parents aren't worried, they know I'll be home in time for supper."

"Where are we going, anyhow?" I asked.

"You wanted to know what my name is? It's easy to remember because Ilan Baum is nothing but two times 'tree'; Ilan means tree and Baum means tree—and what about you? Are you really Pinkas?"

And so, going way back to my beginnings, I told him about myself; the words flowed from me, as my companion floated along beside. Incorporeal, unknown kinsman, central knot in the invisible net—I shall follow you, I shall follow you. I felt as if a portable tent had been constructed around and over me. Ilan told me that his forebears had also come from the Imperial and Royal Austro-Hungarian Monarchy, that his father was a bookbinder by profession, as his father had been before him. "You can live with us," he said. "I'll give you my room; you must not leave here; there is so much you have to learn. We shall learn together. Hey, how old do you think I am?" Ten, fifteen? One of those astonishing beings that seem ageless. "Sixteen?" I ventured. He laughed. "Thirteen and a half, less than half your age. Yet for HaShem, a hundred thousand years are but the blinking of an eye. And as for dying—it's as if you were a twin in your mother's womb. One morning your brother is born into the world, and you are left alone; you think, *oy veh!* my dear brother is dead, he is gone from my world. Up until the moment that you, too, are born, you will think: I have lost my dear brother."

We had arrived at the intersection of Gershon Agron and King George streets. An old woman, bent with age, was waving her cane at a bus driver only a few yards beyond where he had made his last stop. She banged on the windows and door; and when the driver still wouldn't open, she screamed like someone being tortured. At that point, Ilan ran up to the red-and-white bus, stood in the street directly in front of it, and grabbed hold of its old-fashioned radiator grille. Horns blew, pedestrians gathered. "Forget it," someone said, and pointed at the driver, "that's not a human being"; others tried in vain to persuade him to open up, wringing their hands, beating wildly—the door remained closed. I ran to Ilan's side; we braced our feet and leaned against the grille. Angry gestures from the passengers; we nodded and smiled; the bus driver sat on his horn; twenty passersby encircled us. I was surprised at how cool I stayed. We did not relent until three drivers of a truck carrying oxygen tanks got trapped in the traffic jam, climbed out, spat on Ilan, and seized hold of me like a pack of rabid dogs. The bus roared ahead; the old woman stood there, helpless and lost; the line of backed-up cars drove past. A pair of guttersnipes is what we are, I thought; but Ilan still wasn't finished. He hailed a taxi, helped the bent-over woman get in the back, gave the driver some money, and the taxi drove off with a jerk, the rear door still half open. At that moment the howl of a siren cut through the air like an alarm in wartime: it was the shrill Friday-evening signal announcing the start of the Sabbath.

On the main floor of an apartment house in a part of the city called Rehaviah, we entered a little synagogue. Ilan told me I had to empty my pockets and deposit everything in a little niche in the wall behind the door. "Today you are not allowed to carry anything with you; you must be in HaShem's hands without any symbols of security, otherwise you will not feel the Sabbath—no money, no papers, no nothing, you must not even think about them." Evening prayer had already begun—loud lamentation and chanting, a proclamation of sorrow. I wanted to get out of that room, but instead hesitantly handed Ilan my wallet, comb, note pad, ballpoint. "You don't want to stay here," he said, "I can tell that, but please try, Pinkas, please."

My passport! Where was my passport? Hotel lobby? Out of my shirt pocket? When Ilan jumped and hugged me? "You'll just have to go back tomorrow evening; no problem, they'll keep it for you at the hotel; forget it now; it's your duty to act like a king today—forget your little worries."

The men studied us curiously. I stared at the floor, felt drops of sweat coming from my pores. A narrow room, rough floorboards, yellowish walls, network of cracks on them, neon light pouring down from the low ceiling. Hemmed in by these supplicants dressed in black; old wooden desks in front of me, behind me. I was grieved by my ignorance; it seemed to make my whole body glow with shame. I pretended to Ilan that I had no trouble reading along with the others. I turned the pages of a faded, moldy-smelling book whenever I saw my neighbor turning his. When they sat down, I sat down. If they stood up, I stood up. It was like Sunday Mass when my nursemaid Erna used to take me along: rise and kneel whenever the others rose and knelt. A side-glance from Ilan made me giddy—it brought back a dream I had had the night before: In the nave of a church, my relatives and an unrelated group were at prayer, both under the same roof but on opposite sides of the aisle. When a woman knelt and made the sign of the cross, someone who looked very like Ilan suddenly laughed aloud. The woman went to a more remote spot, crossed herself again; we studied her as if she were performing some jungle ritual. We were eating and drinking, that was an important part of our holiday; I was embarrassed in the presence of these strangers for the fact that we didn't want to take our meal in front of the cathedral.

"Mother and I will take good care of you," whispered Ilan; he went back to his prayer, recited loudly, swayed back and forth, more driven even than the men. "He rolls back the light before the darkness," I was reading the text in translation, "and the darkness before the light, and He divided day and night. Praise be to

You, Almighty, Who causes twilight to descend." The men turned to face the rear wall: "You spread yourself out in all directions," they exclaimed. "Welcome, Bride; welcome, Bride!" Thus they received the Sabbath. I was a visitor to another planet, Ilan an alien. It was all a swaying and trembling, peril on the high seas, not an atom of quiet contemplation. The absence of any sense of deliverance in these prayers suffocated me. I remained in the synagogue only for Ilan's sake, only because I was in awe of him. The silence of prayer in churches—how good it used to be in those lofty spaces, within their cool stone walls, alone, kneeling on a low wooden bench, praying my unwritten prayers. How blissful I could feel in a cathedral, in a great church, in a chapel. Here: assaulted by the noise of this synagogue, this tumultuous atmosphere of people being forced to wait for something, this having-to-be-on-earth-without-the-Messiah. And yet, in the church, salvation is only something dangled before the eyes: it is total theater, an illusion to be seen through. Here: noise and restlessness, prayer as though earth were nothing more than a world made of war, suffering, and vileness.

Keys rattled; the men were locking their prayer books in their desks. Near the prayer leader someone raised a goblet of red wine. "Kiddush!" they whispered to each other; "Amen!" they spoke, and gathered together in the narrow corridor. They all shook hands with one another; "Git Shabbes!" they called out. I shook hands, too, stranger in their midst; one question after another was directed at me. I answered each time, "Sholem Aleihem!" "Git Shabbes!" Nothing else; I heard Ilan's voice in the midst of the confusion; he was speaking with a group of elders: ". . . and he tells me he's here for the first time, in Eretz Israel, never had a feeling for his roots before." Ilan was giving away everything I had told him on our walk. "When he was twelve he suddenly made up his mind to learn how to read the Torah. Wait, Pinkas. Don't go away. After the Bar Mitzvah, he decided never to go to shul again; isn't that right, Pinkas?" Someone from the group came up to me. Ilan exclaimed, "Pinkas, this is my father." A powerful man, full beard, head like a living mountain—I saw his great projecting nose, full lips beneath it; he pressed me to his body, stroked the back of my head. "Be welcome. Very good that you have returned, to Eretz Israel, your homeland. I know that place where you grew up; two years ago I visited my nephew there at Yom Kippur."

He began to tell his story, simultaneously taking leave of the other men. We left the synagogue; he had one of his massive arms around Ilan. "He's not living where he belongs, my nephew, but where he became a rich man, and on top of that, in the country where it all happened. He's playing a game of chess with the guilty conscience of the people whose country it is. We go one time to Kol Nidre; never heard such a loud racket in all my life. The rabbi began to speak; a few people kept going shhh! or rapped on the benches, didn't help in the slightest. But the people next to me, I could make out every word they were saying: the horse races, price of gold, of crocodile skins, special sale on coats; not for one second the slightest feeling of being in HaShem's presence, nothing but a fashion show; what a curse I let out against those assimilated people," said Lavan Baum. We were walking down Balfour Street in the gathering darkness. "Enough of cursing now, preserve my tongue from evil, and my lips, that they not utter falsehood. For you should not do unto your neighbor what you would not have them do unto you. The tongue of a man is mightier than his sword, my father always said—a sword can only kill a man who is standing right there, but evil talk can kill a man at the other end of the world. But now *this* year when Yom Kippur comes, one more month— then you'll see what kind of a day that *really* is."

Ilan's mother welcomed us in the entrance hall of a small apartment; she received me as if I were an old acquaintance; her features were very similar to Ilan's. Her dark eyes—they seemed so familiar to me. "We're so used to his bringing people home like this," she said, "mostly from the King David; that's his hunting ground—sometimes even older people; then he makes them spend the night with us." Ilan, rightful teacher of his own parents, gentle king of this little space, showed me his room.

No pictures on the walls, no record player, no television set, no toy cars or plastic Indians. Nothing but piles of books, heaps of magazines, black clothes, writing paper, and ballpoint pens. On one table, a cardboard model of the Second Temple. I thought to myself: if my parents had moved to this land after the Unspeakable happened, would I have become someone like Ilan? "I know what you're thinking. I know what you're thinking," he said, without looking me in the eyes—and I believed him, without asking. He showed me his father's workshop. Tall wooden frames and the tools of his trade, strips of linen and pieces of leather strewn everywhere. On the worktable, mountains of books. Smell of glue and leather.

Gleam of eighteen flames, their fire fed by pure olive oil. "You have chosen us and blessed us among all peoples and granted us your Sabbath in love and affection. Praise be to You, Everlasting, Who sanctifies the Sabbath." Lavan had spoken the blessing over the wine; gave us to drink. (Us *alone* have You chosen, HaShem? I pushed the thought aside.) Lavan blessed the bread, dipped it in the salt, broke off a piece for each of us, passed it along. Ilan in silent jubilation looked at me as his guest at this table. Rivkah told me about her and Lavan's land of birth, recalled the hilly landscape, the deep and fertile soil, which she had lovingly preserved like colored snapshots in her memory for thirty years—since her childhood—without ever wanting to return there.

"Do you know why they hate us so much?"
Lavan asked; I couldn't be sure whom he
meant, but shook my head anyhow. "Because
they know for a fact that we have made a con-
venant with HaShem, and they haven't. We, before all other people, are His possession; we
have a compact with Him. And they have none.
The goyim will come running to us one day,
begging for permission to learn the Torah." An
anxious look out of the corner of Ilan's eye. I
disapproved of that statement—he recognized
it right away; he felt responsible for the words
of his father. I wanted to tell them about Dana
and her relatives, tried to describe the view-
point of the outsiders, and was beginning to
speak of the Armenian Quarter, when Rivkah
signaled me with her eyes that I should first
help myself to more red wine. I reached for the
decorated carafe. Lavan's hand shot out, tore
the bottle from my fingers—he filled my glass.
"Forgive me," Rivkah whispered to him. And
Ilan, white as chalk (did he have tears in his
eyes?), stammered almost inaudibly, "If anyone
has not kept the Sabbath two times in a row, he
may not . . . I know, you don't understand all
this—but he is not supposed to touch the wine
bottle."

"He'll learn that, he'll learn all those things!"
Lavan added in a loud voice. I felt ill, felt the
pain of insult; I wanted to jump up from the
table, leave the apartment. And I stayed there. I
knew again how Dana felt in the circle of my
kinsmen. I wanted to remove the fetters of this

common bondage, tear myself free from such a family chain, no matter how ancient; wanted to call up the King David Hotel, ask them if they had found my passport—then realized, yes, naturally, all telephoning is forbidden on this day. I became flushed. An oval clock on the wall: instead of normal numbers, little plastic roses— all the old furniture revoltingly ugly; how can people live like this? But: next to the wall clock, tall bookcases, wonderful volumes, bound in precious leathers, grouped according to size, gilt lettering on their spines. Painful silence in the room, the Sabbath peace ripped like a silk cloth. At moments like these I tend to look at whatever objects are close at hand, as if every mark on them, every color, held some enormous portent, were the key to my ability to go on breathing. I picked up a silver fork, bent over it, turned it slowly, examined its four tines, its handle, its shell decoration.

"It is written, Genesis, chapter two, '*Al ken yaasov ish et aviv ve et imo. . . .*'" Lavan was speaking with a calm voice. I interrupted him— an urge to be insolent, inflict wound for wound. I insisted that he reformulate what he intended to say, from his heart, without recourse to the Scriptures. "That is to say: the man will leave his father and his mother," Lavan continued, "and he will cleave to his wife and they will become one flesh. Good, *Baruch HaShem*; Ilan will soon leave us; he will marry and become the father of children. If a man wants to live in total union with his wife, he must first cut the umbilical cord that connects him to his parents, otherwise he can never become an independent person." I was drinking the wine in rude gulps; Ilan sat beside me, deflated; he looked quietly into his mother's eyes, so like his own. I didn't leave my parents, I heard myself think, I didn't burn my umbilicus through. We were eating stewed pears. I bent over to look at a copper napkin ring, decorated with light-blue semiprecious stones. "You must get married, Pinkas," said Rivkah. "You are old, could easily have had three children by now." And Lavan, "We'll introduce him to a girl." And Rivkah, "But *frumm*, she's got to be *frumm*, not *frei*." (To be free is the Orthodox opposite of being pious! I laughed.) Calmly I studied the swinging needle of my emotions, read off the numbers as on a gauge inside myself. Like sand slowly settling in water that has been stirred up, my rage sank into more obscure regions—in deference to Ilan. My desire to jump up from the table changed into a wary feeling of having found an anchorage. Our supper table, a framework—I am not driftwood; I am a passenger ship sailing out of a great harbor, underway in any weather, bound for a new shore. With the aid of the red wine, things emerged that I normally knew only from dreams when the body receives messages from the soul that the rational mind doesn't comprehend. Then blood built a bridge between body and soul: *dam* means blood, *adom* means red, *adama*: earth, soil. I am Adam, Your earth-son,

HaShem. Dream is the holy beholding of time compressed; in the dream state, body and soul knew secrets that the waking state extinguished. Like stars above us in the daylight (although I cannot see them), dreams remain within our heads when we're awake, yet stay veiled, until we close our eyes and fall asleep again.

Peaceful, rounded space in which we were sitting; behind the blackness of the clouds is the radiance, I was saying to myself . . . when suddenly all the electric lights in the apartment went out. Blackout, I thought instantly. "You don't know about that?" Rivkah asked, surprised. "You just set the thing for any time you want and it automatically shuts off the current, and we don't have to touch it ourselves—on the Sabbath." Only the oil lamps now shed their light. How well I felt again. Suddenly it seemed so self-evident: the permission to touch the Sabbath wine bottle only after I observe the holy day with all my heart. The spines of the books, the bars of my dungeon; in my jaws I felt reins being tugged; they let me run; then pulled me up short; and let me run again, in the walled-in outlet. Lavan said, "I make you a prophecy: if you leave this place where you belong and run back into the other world—leaving here is called *yeridah*, descent, did you know that?—then when you are there, you will begin to keep this day holy."

"Because you will understand that this day is our umbilical cord to HaShem," said Rivkah, "the only day without machines, without money, without following orders—but in exchange for that, a day for reading with awareness, for conversation, for taking walks. With everything you have in you, you can feel that HaShem is Lord of the world, not we. The Sabbath is not only a day for rest; it's there so you can feel that you're a small part of the whole and discover that during the week you'd had little time to think about that. It's like being in a capsule, quietly anticipating the age that will come with the Messiah."

"How can the goyim seriously believe—I can't get it into my head—how can they believe that the Messiah has already come?" Lavan asked. "Isn't it written as clear as day—look it up in Isaiah: 'And he shall judge between the nations'—goyim means nations—'and shall decide for many peoples; and they shall beat their swords into plowshares, and their spears into pruning hooks; nation shall not lift up sword against nation, neither shall they learn war any more.' Is that what it looks like now in the world? Tell me." And as they were saying these things, I knew: Torah is the Word which has become the People. Proclaimed not only to a caste of priests, HaShem's Revelation through Moshe Rabeinu has been passed along to every man, to every woman, an eternally new reality, transmitted for three thousand five hundred years. In Ilan, Lavan, Rivkah, it has become flesh and blood, taken up into their hearts letter for letter, every word still in its pure meaning, not patched up with the sludge of today's world. "Do you know that it is written," said Lavan, "if all of Israel were to keep holy the Sabbath only two times running, the Messiah would appear on earth at once?"

Bordered for a distance by single-story houses built of some light-colored stone, an anonymous, unpaved road climbed steadily uphill through olive groves, illuminated by the gray light of a half moon. Ilan had managed to get permission to take this evening walk with me. I envied his alertness; he seemed so much more lively, stronger than me, his stride more energetic, more rhythmic. Mud clung to the soles of our shoes, made our footsteps heavy.

"Everything is in HaShem's hands, everything—except our fear of Him," Ilan said, interrupting our silence. By now I had learned to speak the Word-that-had-become-the-People, to carry it further. I replied, "And if you come down on the side of evil, HaShem will help you up, just as if you had come down on the side of good."

"Bravo, congratulations!" Ilan exclaimed, laughed aloud, pointed with both hands up into the endless sky above. "You've become a regular *bocher*. Soon you'll be putting on tefillin; prayer will give you strength you never knew you had. No question of it, you will observe the next Sabbath. Promise me you will!" He hugged me tight with one arm, "Promise me you will?" I gave a sort of half-nod, more like a shaking of the head than a real nod of agreement.

We had reached the summit of the Hill of Talpiot, marched along the flat, gravelly road; I scraped the mud still clinging to my shoes on the sharp edges of the little stones. Silhouettes of the city surrounded by its hills, image of the universal dream, packaged in an inky-blue, transparent membrane. I let myself fly out over the Old City, over the New City, like a falcon, and I hovered there, suspended over the most solemn city on earth. From this height its two parts flowed together, the past into its future, like music. Nothing was in the present, yet everything was, everything simultaneous—when David ruled the city, some ancestor stood on this very spot, let himself float down on the wings of his panoramic gaze. And in the coming millennium our children's children will stand on this same spot and let this mere city become again the City Everlasting as once their forebears did. "Every stone here is your possession, a building stone of your own house." Ilan spoke very softly and pointed down to the plateau where the Temple once stood and to the Hill of Moriah where Abraham was commanded to sacrifice Isaac. All the anxiety on earth emanates from this mount, the legend tells us. "Stay here, for if you do not you will seek and seek all your life long and never find another home. *Hashgahah pratit*, your own special providence, brought you here. This is where you belong." He moved a little away from me, left his words with me as if they were beings in their own right. I felt certain then that this was a moment I already knew, had lived through, from another past, from another future perhaps. Foreknowledge? Forgotten past? . . .

Suddenly a man darted at us out of the darkness, not old, not young, neither a small man nor a big one; well dressed, in gray, with a black hat on his head; first went up to Ilan and then brushed very close to me, my heart beat wildly; the stranger stopped a short distance away, and cried out to us, "Woe! From its rising unto its setting, woe! Woe to all who are bridegroom and bride, woe unto all the people! They beat me for crying out this way, but I do not ask for mercy. My voice does not grow hoarse and I cry out: Woe from its rising unto its setting, woe to Yerushalayim!" Shivers ran from the nape of my neck down my back. I looked around to find Ilan. The stranger with his odd hopping gait stopped once more, shouted louder than ever, "Woe from its rising, woe from its setting, woe to Yerushalayim!" and disappeared from view. Ilan returned calmly. "You were frightened by him? I've known him for some time, he runs around everywhere shouting, always the same words. He's called Joshua, no one knows where he comes from, he never answers if you ask him something." Gradually I calmed down, looked again out over our city, beyond the horizon of night. Chips of stone, that is what we are, molecules in Your sight, HaShem. "Where matter ends, what comes after that, what lies beyond?"

asked my soul-twin, as if I knew the answer. From far away a wail resounded one final time, "Woe unto Yerushalayim!"

Downhill under tall cypress trees. Like me, Ilan seemed never to take the same way back. The scratchy chirp of cicadas filled the air. Smell of dust and tree bark. A frightened feeling, like a viscous mass, was still inside me. Ilan said, "This is what we must proclaim to the world, with a quiet but penetrating voice: If we take man to be the measure of all things, how mean, how dubious everything becomes. HaShem is the measure of all things. Return to Him. As Jonah once warned the city of Nineveh, so must we warn the world today, 'Our world will perish if we do not retrace our steps.' Flight into outer space, do you know what that is? It's nothing more than fear of the new flood of fire. Spaceships are the new arks. A New Age is coming and this city will be its fountainhead. HaShem will reveal Himself here. We must be prepared for that. This New Age can begin without catastrophe, without a second Deluge, through a great return to Him." My teacher grew silent, walked ahead without soliciting the acknowledgment of my glance. "Your monologues sound as if you were speaking to yourself sometimes, or like prepared speeches," I said, but Ilan's equanimity could not be upset. "All talk is a talking to HaShem," he replied. "Look, everything that exists is remote, buried very deep. Who will find it?"

The residential area of Abu Tor; fragrance of

oranges spreading out from the circumference of a single tree. Laurel bushes. Sound of insects. A dusty street named En Rogel. The train station nearby. My amazement at my rabbi increased step by step. My silent, my inner reaction was envy and awe. Or could it have been that I was making Ilan into my mentor simply because my other half needed a teacher, that part of me that yearned to put the yoke of the Law on its shoulders? When he caught sight of the oranges there was such radiant happiness in his eyes, of a kind that I had not known myself since I was a child. Clasping his hands behind his back, he inhaled the fragrance. I wanted to offer him one of the fruits, stuck a hand in among the branches. Ilan's hand gently admonished mine, only then did I remember: picking, harvesting, too, are forbidden on this day, be it only a single ear of wheat, one leaf, one blade of grass—be it an orange. "But people, when they see the rings of Saturn, or a piece of fruit, a bee, an eye," Ilan continued as we walked along, "then they say, that came from nothing, by accident, cell by cell, millions of years, infinity arose from nothing. And if they admit that, yes, there must have been some first cell—Where then did this first cell come from?—then they say, chemical processes. And where do these chemical processes come from? Then they break off the conversation. But when they discover an ancient bottle buried in the ground, or a fork, or a knife, then right away they say, Someone made that." I replied that my own doubt was very great, too. I could never comprehend, I said, that *that* could have happened, forty years ago, only three decades before Ilan was born. We went along without speaking; for a long while the only thing to be heard was the echo of our footsteps.

As we walked past the shunting tracks of the station my rabbi spoke. "You will be . . . I think you will be horrified at what I am feeling now. I must figure out how to . . . it's hard to find the right words. You know that the Everlasting, may His Name be praised, gave us a promise; if we keep faith with His Torah, he will protect us always and be benevolent to us and multiply our people. But if you do not obey my Commandments, says the Everlasting, then you shall be accursed among all people into whose hands I shall deliver you. He will send a people upon our heads from the ends of the earth, one which soars like an eagle—so it is written: like an *eagle*—an insolent people who take no heed of the old and do not spare the young. If we take up the customs of the alien people, HaShem will hide His face from us and deliver us into the hands of our adversaries. To be chosen does not mean to be better, it means we have to assume a greater burden of responsibility. And never since HaShem first spoke to us, never has disregard of His Commandments been so great as in this century. And where has it been worst of all, this assimilation of ours, where? In those very countries where later the Unspeakable happened. HaShem carried out

His threat. That one lunatic and his hench-men—the only thing they will be known for in days to come is that it was they who wanted to obliterate us—they were the tools in HaShem's hands, they were . . ."

"Ilan," I shouted, "stop! That's enough now. The others, the ones who kept to the absolute letter of the Law, they, too, were murdered and burned in exactly the same way." I stammered, I was assailed by a shuddering chill. Who is this boy, where do these words of his come from? "The good will perish along with the others," he replied calmly. "They failed to battle with all their might against the evil, they were ac-complices. HaShem wants us to *live*, we wouldn't be here otherwise. Yes, the world stood and stared at our incineration, and it would simply stare again if something like it should happen to the nation where we live now. But this time there's a difference: If Yerushalayim perishes, then the whole earth will perish. That Great War was the final warn-ing HaShem gave man to reverse his course. And once again it was *we* who were the sign He gave, His people, chosen and raised up as His example. If the return does not take place soon, the entire earth will be burned to ashes next time. We must go on a journey, out into the fear-racked world, and admonish it to return."

A bundle of tears was forming at the roof of my mouth. Exhaustion, agitation, like a child on the threshold of a separation. I wanted to shake Ilan by the shoulders, embrace him. Had

I only imagined the words he spoke, had I infused my own thoughts into him, a vessel I had found? After a long march back, we passed by the city theater, shut now these twenty-four hours. Standing next to a closed café, two young men with their long-haired and luminous girl friend, probably just passing through, I could hear them cursing the strict observance of the holy day; one of the boys pressed his mouth against the girl's lips; the other part of me, that other half, entered his bones, seized and lifted the shining girl in a deep embrace. As if none of the thoughts and words between Ilan and me had occurred only minutes before, I suddenly longed to travel through the night with these three friends, to be naked with them, and I began to formulate a sentence in my brain to help dislodge myself from Ilan, so swiftly did my focus shift. I was already no longer at his side by the time he turned the corner into Oliphant Street; the three messengers were behind me arm in arm, and I ran to catch up with Ilan, to say goodbye to him quickly. He was standing in front of the apartment house. I didn't want to enter the building. "You will be staying the night with me, won't you? I'm sure my parents have put an extra bed in my room." His voice sounded compressed. The words stuck like a blade between the two halves of my split nature, slashed the road before me into a path that forked. I wanted to stay with him. I decided to leave. I wanted to stay with him. "You don't know what you want," he said.

"You're looking for something and trying at the same time not to find it. . . ." Was he about to cry? "But what you are really looking for you will find." Or was it I who was the one close to tears? "Where do you think you can go now in the middle of the night? Come, please, you haven't said goodbye to my parents, come. And early in the morning we'll go to the mikvah, you've never been to a mikvah yet, have you? And then afterwards to the synagogue." Ilan could see that I wasn't going to be staying with him. "You are going to ruin your Sabbath. You don't know much yet. At least swear to me that you will go on learning. Put on the tefillin, wear them. Buy them Sunday, buy them right away." I grew impatient with him; I didn't want to put on tefillin, I explained, not if I couldn't believe that HaShem spoke to us from Mount Sinai. "You're not supposed to *believe*, you're supposed to *know*, you've only forgotten. You must learn, learn, then you'll remember." I laughed sadly. "Do you want to keep running away all your life? The things you've learned since you've been here, they're things that will never leave you. Up to now, ignorance isolated you from the Law; but now you know what they mean, the Commandments, some of them." I leaned down and pressed my forehead against his shoulder, felt his hand on the back of my head, pulled away from my brother. "You have to come and get your things at the temple, you know. You'll come by tomorrow evening, promise?" I turned away, tore myself away, fork in the road, looked back once more; in the darkened stairwell he was climbing up to the home of his parents.

My steps took me through a little barren park. Not a trace of the three strangers I was looking for. A green bird dead in the gravel. I was wearing phrases, words of wisdom, over my shoulders and they hung down both sides, still untied; I could not bind their fringes. I should have spent the night with my brother; why did I not stay with him? My pockets empty. I liked being without money, without anything to write with, anything to write on. But if the world was not created in six days, why then Sabbath every seventh day? Why not six hundred million years of work and a hundred million years of Sabbath? That You rule the earth, HaShem, that You created the universe (why did You create the universe?)—was I put into this world to *comprehend* all of that? The sky clear, full of stars, to the north a storm brewing. I longed for my teacher, decided to turn back—didn't turn back. A hundred flashes of lightning in a bank of clouds. Not a sound of thunder in the cool air, too far away. Like the flickering of artillery. You are making flames, HaShem, You? On the Sabbath? This lightning, forged in the days of Creation, and released now, today, in this place? Across a narrow valley to my right, Mount Zion and the walls of the Old City, illuminated by electricity— beyond them churches, domes, battlements. The Citadel of Herod. Jaffa Gate. . . . No passport! I had forgotten that I had lost my passport. . . . Who am I? Why no brothers, no sisters, and why no friends, no wife, no children, one day no parents? To enter the Law will help me alleviate my loneliness, but I do not want to have to invent You out of my own weakness, HaShem. Where am I to go? Woe unto Yerushalayim, woe also unto me. "The voice of the Everlasting divides the flames of the fire. The voice of the Everlasting shakes the wilderness. The voice of the Everlasting makes the oaks whirl and strips the forests bare, and in His temple every one speaks of His glory." I didn't know how it went on.

Through a high revolving door into the brilliantly lit lobby of the King David Hotel. (One more proof of the fact that the earth is round, some forefather of mine is said to have declared each time he took his constitutional and returned home.) Lobby tall as a house—a home and refuge. Far away, a man sunk into a leather armchair was playing a game of chess with an invisible opponent. I looked for the night porter, could not understand how one of the grandest hotels in the city could be left with no guard at its entrance, until I saw that little camera high overhead, oscillating from side to side, secured to a gilded beam. An elevator door snapped open with a loud sound, no one had rung for it. The hand on a clock face jumped one marker to one-forty-four. I entered the elevator; even before I could push a floor button the door closed, the cabin whooshed to the second floor. The door opened, closed by itself, the elevator went up to the third floor. Without my touching a single button I ascended floor by floor to the top. I was in a Sabbath elevator that conducted its passenger from floor to floor without his having to complete the electric circuit, without his having so much as a hand in the making of the future. (And even with this, the true observants walked the staircase up to their rooms on this holy day.) I ran back down the carpeted steps to the ground floor, met on the fourth floor one of the ladies to whom I had loaned my newspaper that afternoon; she was wearing a silk nightgown that hung down to her ankles, leaned against the elaborately curved stair railing; it looked like a scene in the belly of an old ocean liner.

The night porter, a balding man with the bushiest eyebrows I had ever seen, was drying his hands on the entire contents of a packet of Kleenex. When I told him about my lost passport he looked at me with a combination of gentle concern and glee at my loss. He disappeared behind a column, made metallic clinking noises with his bunch of keys, didn't reemerge for a long time. The seconds seemed as immense and endless as the corridors of the hotel. Then he leaned over the reception desk, his face close to mine, holding the open passport in his hand, compared photograph with fact. "Well—hmm. Good. Just one thing though—this country you call your own country up there, it's like a wife, yes? You're married but you don't know if it's forever, right? Will she cheat on you, will you cheat on her? But if you belong to *our* country, then she's like a mother to you. No escaping, nix. And cheating on her? You couldn't, even if you should happen to try." His loud laugh lasted only a second. The elevator arrived at the ground floor, doors snapped open automatically. In the far background the chess player. The night porter handed me my Diaspora pass. The elevator doors snapped shut. The night porter winked. I wanted to give him a reward for finding it, remembered that I had no money with me, blushed, broke out in perspiration, made a pretense of going through all my pockets, stammered some excuse or other and something about the Sabbath, whereupon the night porter exploded once again with his laugh, so loud, so brief, turned his back on me, vanished behind a column. I wanted to call out something to him and didn't do it. Out onto the street. Longing for my brother Ilan. I jogged off in the direction of Zion Square—over there not far away, the apartment house where Rachel lived.

9.

. . . JOGGING ALONG, away from this desert of gravel. The conscious act of walking has the power to level its own path. I have left my walking stick behind. Like an awakening after a flashback is over—inner images give way again to those of the real world outside. I am watching myself, standing beside a bush; it is colorless, smells of dried-fruit bars. Smells are the bread of the soul. I shall remember this moment in the world to come, or so I imagine. I shall return to this bush, to myself, and stand next to myself, invisibly here, on this street. In the world to come I shall have to relive the splendor along with the unendurable from this life that I have led. I shall have to relive them, again and again—the completion of circles serves only to generate new ones. The wound on my knee is bleeding. I'm proud of this token. Blood ooozes through the leg of my trousers. A group of young scouts in a field; I walk past them whistling, the girls giggle, everything familiar, everything alien to me; a little boy runs up to me from another direction and says,

"You aren't supposed to whistle on holy days."
"Hey, you're right," I answer; stop whistling at once. I head for an intersection, search the sidewalk, search next to the tree trunks and along the curb, poke through the litter collected around sewer gratings and under soggy newspapers, even in the middle of the street I search for that one significant object: the matchbox. And don't find it. Brakes squeal, shudder; horns blow. Not until that moment do I realize where I am—the bread bakery, over there. Same humming factory sound. And just a little farther along, the street where I live. I hadn't even recognized it. To feel one's own soul is a frightening thing to me; it rubs against me, tears at me; feeling your own living soul, the way it lies in there, naked, in its envelope, its scaffolding that protects it and at the same time robs it of its power to see. It lies embedded in flesh and blood, like a fruit inside its own skin; it listens to you, it feels you; and I feel it, it lives there naked in my cell. Walking along, I test my various senses: I suck on a peppermint candy to find out if perhaps my sense of taste has changed. Wash my wound in very cold water from a hydrant. Stop walking; smell leaves and branches; stare intently at everything around me; listen intently to every sound; walk along a low fence rail at a playground—and try to keep my balance. Not having a third eye at the back of my head is part of Your scheme to remind us that You exist, part of Your plan. For if I did have it, that third eye,

I would surely deny You. It is written: at the onset of the Age of the Messiah the children will teach their parents the Torah. It is written: this city will be the wellspring of the New World, a light unto the nations, the Order will emanate from Zion. Yes, I shall flirt with the Law—I can already see it coming. This city: is it to become my earthly midpoint?

Without moving a muscle, in agitated repose, I stand before the apartment house where I live. Is this the house where I live? Does the soul maintain the body as HeSheIt maintains the world? In dark sunlight, as I stand before this house, You give me the long evening shadows to drink, HaShem. From the top of my head to the soles of my feet I am showered with Your gifts. You are patient. You allow me to grope my way. You have planted Your Word in me. You trickle through the smoke. What do You want of me? How do You want me to be? You, Chosen One, do You pray, too? Do You pray? Perhaps You pray, too. I lack the courage to pluck myself out, to enter into the Law. I do not want to have to renounce the details and particulars of the world. I want to be seated at the focal point of the end of the millennium, my eyes wide open. You have revealed Yourself, Your Word exists, even when I am unable to believe? And before my departure I shall buy the prayer thong and as a sign I shall bind it to my arm and between my eyes. A mezuzah is fastened to the doorpost, a tiny metal box with a prayer parchment rolled up inside; I have *paid it no attention until this moment—but now, as I enter the apartment building, I touch it. Jets scream overhead. I kiss the tips of my fingers: this box transforms the building into Your Temple. And very slowly I climb the stairs to the sixth floor—*Shema Yisrael Adonai Eloheinu Adonai Ehad. *Thou, listen, Thou One and Only, Everlasting: I love Thee with all my heart and with all my soul and with all my strength. Will You banish us from here, too? I am leaving Your city now, shall not stay here for Yom Kippur (in seven days, Yom Kippur). Thou hast not yet sent us the Messiah? Exodus without end? Is this planet my homeland? Shall I begin to observe the dietary laws? Shall I begin to honor the Sabbath? Shall I? Yerushalayim, beloved, is one of my ribs. The door to the apartment is double-locked. The apartment I have been sharing is empty now, not a soul. It smells of smoke and food. On the floor, my gaping suitcases. My Inner Homeland, have I reached it?*